THEOLOGY, PHYSICS, AND MIRACLES

THEOLOGY, PHYSICS, AND MIRACLES

Werner Schaaffs

Translated by
Richard L. Renfield

Canon Press
Washington, D.C.

Title of the original German edition:
THEOLOGIE UND PHYSIK VOR DEM WUNDER
Copyright © 1973 by R. Brockhaus Verlag
Wuppertal

ISBN # 0 913686 17 4
Copyright © 1974 by Canon Press
1014 Washington Building
Washington, D.C. 20005
Printed in the United States of America

FOREWORD

This is an age of science, an age of materialism, an age that focuses on what can be seen, felt, heard, and handled. It is also an age of luxury, convenience, and ease, much of which has come through scientific discovery. Consequently man, with his pragmatic orientation, has come to worship at the altar of science. Because science has given us such great gifts, it is to be worshipped: it is to be our god replacing the outmoded God of the Bible. Thus, men once more worship and serve the creature rather than the Creator.

Because it is an age of science, it is also an age of skepticism, for science is characterized by skepticism. Ideally at least, the scientist is ready to question any accepted truth. Scientific progress has come largely by questioning the accepted truths of past generations. It is inevitable that this skepticism should be applied also to religion and to the very foundation of the Christian religion, the Scriptures themselves.

Not the least of the values of this little book is its value as the confession of an orthodox Christian who is also a scientist of the first water. The author has worked on the frontiers of science. He knows physics, generally recognized as the most advanced of the sciences, as few men of our age do. Yet he is a humble Christian, and his book is the open, unabashed confession of a man who accepts the faith in its orthodox evangelical sense. He finds no difficulty in accepting Jesus Christ as his own personal Saviour and the Saviour of the world, and he looks forward to the Resurrection and to the bliss of heaven.

Schaaffs' main purpose is to show that the objections to miracles of the so-called modern theologians and their insistence on interpreting Scripture as a collection of myths are based on an outmoded science. They have come to accept the universe as a closed system and to deny the possibility of any intervention by God. This was all very fine so far as the physics of the nineteenth and the early twentieth century were concerned.

As Schaaffs points out, it was possible then to believe that only the material had reality and that strict cause and effect ruled the universe. This point of view is completely outmoded. He suggests that "modern" theologians are not looking forward but backward to the nineteenth century. His analysis is devastating. As a committed Christian he finds it embarrassing not only to be told, but also to find it to be true, that scientists confess and testify to their Christian faith whereas theologians lie, deceive, and mislead.

Schaaffs' book also calls our attention to the wonder of the natural. Many evangelical Christians have fallen into the pattern of overemphasizing God's working supernaturally and minimizing the significance of his working naturally. Somehow or other we have gotten the idea that when God works naturally, through means, through the natural laws which he established at creation, his working is not nearly so wonderful as when he intervenes directly in the affairs of the universe. Schaaffs reflects the awe that a scientist feels when he sees the intricacies and complexities of the universe which God has created. It is another significant contribution of Schaaffs' book that he calls our attention to the wonder of God's working through the natural laws which he has established and asks us to stand in awe at his wisdom and power in setting these up.

By calling our attention to developments in modern physics Schaaffs also demonstrates the possibility and plausibility of the miracles that occur in Scripture. It is certainly true that our acceptance of the scriptural account does not depend on its possibility or plausibility; yet it is helpful to us to know that such a possibility exists even when we look at these occurrences from a "natural" standpoint. Christianity is not based on logic and reasonableness: it is based on faith. Still, the understanding that what we believe is not contrary to reason even though it may be beyond reason and understanding is helpful.

This book is also helpful in demonstrating the unity of all knowledge. Schaaffs shows that a compartmentalization of knowledge is not necessary. The scientist need not put aside his theology when he goes into the laboratory nor must he deny what he has learned in his scientific studies when he reads the Scriptures or worships with his fellow believers. There is a basic unity to all knowledge, and this is true of the knowledge revealed in Scripture as well as of the knowledge revealed in the laboratory. It is not necessary to put aside what one knows by revelation when one seeks knowledge on the frontiers of science through his senses and his reason, as if these two could not possibly agree or be reconciled.

Yet there are some areas in which many evangelical Christians, including the undersigned, will wish to take issue with Professor Schaaffs. He does well in demonstrating that the miracles of Scripture are plausible, but he goes too far when he seeks to demonstrate that natural explanations are adequate for an understanding of most if not all of the so-called miracles of the Scriptures. It is all very true, as he points out, that the natural laws that God set up are "very good," and it is also true that God ordinarily works through these natural laws which he established at creation. When we are ill it is ordinarily through the operation of the natural laws governing the workings of our bodies that we recover. But it is a mistake to limit God to these natural laws which he has established, and it is because they know he is not limited that Christians pray.

It seems somewhat inconsistent, too, that Schaaffs is unwilling to accept the historicity of the Genesis account, especially since he makes so much of the statements in the first chapter of Genesis that God saw what he had made and it was good, and especially of Genesis 1:31, "God saw everything that he had made, and behold, it was very good." Schaaffs finds no contradiction between the Genesis account and Darwinian evolution, specifically what he calls "the principle of development." Yet it is very clear that our Lord accepts the historicity of the first chapters of Genesis, for in his controversies with the Pharisees regarding marriage and divorce he quotes from both the first and second chapters of Genesis.

It is equally clear that St. Paul accepts the historicity of our first parents, for he compares Adam and Christ. The Reformation principle has always been that Scripture interprets Scripture. If we accept this principle, the historicity of Adam and Eve cannot be denied in the light of the New Testament references to them as individuals. Schaaffs' objections to special creation and his acceptance of biological evolution seem to be based on scientific principles and evidences which I believe to be outmoded in the same sense that the physics of the nineteenth and early twentieth century is outmoded. Readers may be interested in evaluating the evidence and the judgments presented in my *Genes, Genesis, and Evolution* (St. Louis: Concordia, 1970).

In spite of such strictures Schaaffs' book is a significant contribution to evangelical literature. His description of modern physics is simple and understandable, and he does a valuable service in relating it to theology and to the Scriptures. To know that one's faith is not unreasonable is helpful even though scientific evidences and understandings cannot be the basis for that faith and even though the biblical claim for miracles goes beyond the natural.

John W. Klotz, Professor of
Practical Theology and
Dean of Academic Affairs,
Concordia Seminary, St. Louis,
Missouri

A WORD FROM THE PUBLISHER

There are many natural scientists who are biblical Christians, and many biblical Christians who are natural scientists. But it is very rare for a single individual to combine, as Professor Werner Schaaffs does, research in physics that has earned him a place in the first rank of that exacting science, with a frank, forthright and unambiguous testimony to his faith in Jesus Christ and to the reliability of the biblical record. This is a difficult position to occupy, for it renders one subject to mis-understanding and criticism from both fellow-scientists and fellow-believers. Professor Schaaffs has expressed serious reservations about the appropriateness of certain criticisms contained in the appreciation of this work by Professor Klotz. He fears that such criticism subjects his apologetic and interpretive work to a critique based on dogmatic presuppositions rather than on its scientific merits. Nevertheless, the publisher feels that it is not wrong to preface this book with such observations, for all Christians should agree that no human interpretation of the Bible, however valuable, is to be accepted dogmatically, as irrefragable, nor, as it were, as the ultimate argument that finally overcomes the problem of transcendental, biblical faith in a secularistic world of thought.

Harold O. J. Brown

TABLE OF CONTENTS

PREFACE

I am often invited to speak on the relationship between the biblical miracles and physics. In this book I have assembled my thoughts on the subject. Hence the book is an apologia, in which a physicist defends biblical statements in terms of one of the gifts named in I Corinthians 12 and Ephesians 4, and parries doctrines which strip them of their original meaning and set them down as myths or mythological discourse. My book is addressed to Christians of all denominations.

The martyr Origen (185-254), one of the greatest theologians of the early church, once said, "The difficulties of religion are only those of nature." Hence we may also say, "The difficulties of theology are only those of science." But just as Origen did not deviate from Jesus' instruction, "Search the scriptures, for . . . they are they which testify of me" (John 5:39, A.V.), so must we never cease learning that there is one and only one Creator behind theology and physics. In this task our spirit must be that of which Proverbs 20:27 says, "The spirit of man is the lamp of the Lord, searching all his innermost parts."

The small numbers interspersed through my text refer to the publications listed in the brief bibliography at the end of the book. These references are intended for the reader who not only takes the Bible seriously, but who also wishes to learn something more about the various questions of physics that are raised. Since Christian congregations are often inundated with books and journal articles quite void of any objective rendering or even acceptance of true physics and biology, I feel that such references are needed. If we wish to counter unbiblical theologies and materialistic doctrines effectively, we must arm ourselves with weapons from the arsenals of twentieth-century physics, not with bows and arrows.

Berlin-Siemensstadt, Christmas 1972

W. Schaaffs

1

I. INTRODUCTION

As our subject indicates, we shall be dealing with questions and problems in which theology and physics not only meet but overlap. It lies in an interesting and exciting area. It is exciting in the first place because theology and physics have given rise over the years to sharply divergent views on miracles. Contradictory opinions are still expressed not only by the people below the pulpit or outside its reach but by those in the pulpit as well. They range between the extremes of "divine revelation necessary for salvation," and "physically impossible human myths."

It is therefore only natural that people who grew up with the religious doctrine that categorizes each and every miracle as a supernatural event, arising from God's will and contradicting physics, are later so jarred by the realities of science and technology that they come to doubt, and then fully cast aside, the Holy Scriptures. It is equally natural that other people, finding no peace in science and technology and searching for definitive certainty and truth, are hamstrung by the fact that the doctrines of the Christian faith are so encumbered with ideas based solely on tired old habits and prejudices and advanced in direct contradiction with physics and daily experience.

I should like to try in my own way to show that a man engaged in the problems of modern science or, as an engineer or scientist, dependent on science for his living, is by no means required to turn his back on his childhood faith (as we should not hesitate to call it). He must merely be ready to take the Scriptures really seriously and to think and meditate on these matters. Thought is of the essence of the human spirit and, like that spirit, is itself a gift of the Creator.

As the reader has undoubtedly noticed, my intent is not to give a neutral report on the subject but to commit myself personally. A personal witness as a scientist and physicist by profession seems to me more sincere and meaningful, for it does not sidestep those questions which, in the last resort, are decisive. If I claim to be a Christian and yet refuse to undertake the task of preparing this testimony, I commit a sin. Most of our sins lie not in the faulty or unjust things we do but in the good things we fail to do. When I use the word "sin" in this book, I am referring to the "don't-worry-about-it" philosophy which, while unfortunately innate in us, puts some distance, however politely, between us and God. As the Lord's brother James wrote in his letter, "Whoever knows what is right to do and fails to do it, for him it is sin." My hope here is to do good for our congregations by providing them with useful scientific equipment, not obsolete weapons.

II. THEOLOGY

If one studies the history of the use and development of the concept "theology" from the earliest times to the present and considers the weight and standing that the concept has enjoyed and acquired over the years, one concludes that the high point occurred in the early Christian church with the Gospel according to St. John and the three great confessions of faith—the Apostles' Creed, the Nicene Creed, and the Athanasian Creed. Theology being understood at the time as biblical theology, guidelines were drawn that remain valid today and that have repeatedly enabled the Christian community to orient itself and to recognize erroneous lines of development. The author of this book personally subscribes to this theology. Only by reading the book can one come to know what that means in detail and what its consequences are.

It is certain, however, that this understanding of theology has to a large extent faded from the mind of the general public today. Theology is understood more in heathen, philosophical, and socialist terms, though many young people are not fully aware of this; lacking a solid background in the Bible or the creeds, they believe that the Scriptures do not define theology and that therefore no binding definition of the term exists. It is true that the word "theology" is not found in the Bible, but then neither is "church," for example, nor a number of other important terms. The word *ekklesia,* which we translate "church," actually means "the called out [assembly]." What is important is that all of the fundamental tenets of biblical faith that comprise the content of the laconic expression "biblical theology" do have the same, consistent meaning throughout Scripture. They all make statements that are distinctively different from the assertions of non-Christian re-

5

ligions and other philosophies, and this difference enables us to recognize that the church really is "called out," i.e., something new and distinctive, not the product of its cultural context.

Hence the word "theology" in the title of this book reflects both the author's view that biblical theology is consistent with physics on the subject of miracles on one hand and the clash between the current attenuated, widespread view of theology and the achievements of physics on the other.

The word "theology" derives from the two Greek words *theos* ("god" or "deity") and *logos* ("word" or "precept"). Therefore theology is generally understood as simply a doctrine of God, and of course such a doctrine in some form exists among all peoples and races. There are certainly many similarities among the various religions; it would seem to be a function of "theology" to elaborate the commonalities that unite and to place them at the center of human thought. But that is also what philosophy seeks and achieves, for philosophers—as the Greek roots signify—are "friends of wisdom." Many people, and sometimes universities as well, therefore subordinate theology to philosophy. I think they are justified in doing so, especially in view of the existentialist theology that is actually accepted today as Christian, but is even more prized as timely and modern.

But what is theology as the author understands it, in the light of the New Testament? In his interpretation, too, the "theo-" means God, but it is the one and only God, the God of Abraham, Isaac, and Jacob, the Father of Jesus Christ. The second half denotes the "Logos," the Word. In this theology, God and the Word are one. He uses the word theology to refer to revealed, biblical theology. John the Evangelist describes and explains this unity between God and the Word in the introductory words of his Gospel. From the very first lines of his Gospel he goes far beyond the vision of Matthew, Mark, and Luke. For good reason he was Jesus' favorite disciple. He appears to have been the one who most deeply grasped the essence of theology and who understood his Master best. But it apparently took some time before he attained the maturity that enabled him to go down in church history as the prophet of the fourth Gospel and of Revelation. That occurred about two generations after Pentecost and one generation after the martyrdom of Peter, Paul, and Jesus' brother James. Thus, in the so-called Muratorian Canon of the second century, a sort of foreword or introduction for the Bible used in Roman congregations, it is said of John that "all is explained by this one leading spirit above all others." John was therefore nicknamed *Hagios Theologos,* or the "Holy Theologian."

Of course John begins his Gospel with the words, "In the beginning was the Word, and the Word was with God, and the Word was God." Three assertions are made here. Two are introductory, but the emphasis is on the third. The first and second halves of the term "theology" are made inseparable! The first half refers to a person with clearcut outlines; the second refers to a spiritual state which fills and governs the universe and manifests itself in creative effects. One senses immediately the tremendous difference between the interpretation of theology in the sentence "the Word was God" and the noncommittal interpretation—more acceptable to the men of this world—as "teachings of a deity." One senses that John's theology is dealing with a rock of faith that hell itself could not destroy.

John continues, "All things were made through him (i.e., through the Word), and without him was not anything made that was made." Therefore theology is a profound scholarly field of knowledge and revelation. Yet, says John, it has been made so intimate a part of us that not only the scholar and the priest but even the simplest man can grasp it. John attests to that with the words, "And the Word became flesh and dwelt among us, full of grace and truth; we have beheld his glory. . . ." God became a man, and the man was named Jesus Christ. In this way the first half of the word "theology" becomes more comprehensible to us. But the second half, too, has been placed within our reach and experience. For how does the logos—the Word—speak to us? Through the Holy Spirit! In chapters 14-16 of his Gospel John conveys to us at length what Jesus says on the subject. We learn there that the Holy Spirit is the Spirit of Truth.

The Spirit teaches us what there is to know about the person of Jesus. He teaches us that Jesus speaks to us in the New *and* the Old Testament. We are told in John 16:13 that he will guide us into all truth. Since Jesus himself says that he is the truth, the Holy Spirit leads us again and again to the person of Jesus. The Spirit belongs to the body of Jesus, and through the Spirit Jesus is in the world today. In this form Jesus is in us and around us and closer to us than the air we breathe. True, we do not see Jesus as a person in the time between the Ascension and the Second Coming, but we can hear and feel his Holy Spirit. The Holy Scripture presents the Holy Spirit as so real, present, and knowable that Matthew 12:31,32 and Luke 12:10 describe speaking against him or blaspheming him as unforgivable. A theology attesting to these things keeps me from distorting Samuel's request (I Samuel 3:9,10), "Speak, Lord, for thy servant hears" into "Hear, Lord, for thy servant speaks." In my view, these two sentences underline the difference between an existential interpretation of the Bible, as commanded by the Lord, and the existentialist interpretation, deriving from human philosophies and wishes, which today is considered modern.

There are many ways to present this theology and to extol it through its applications. A pastor will do so with different data and words than a natural scientist, a physician, an econo-mist, or a social worker. For two reasons I shall do so in this book as a physicist. First, it is my profession to study nature and report the results. Second, it is in the events called miracles that theology and physics touch most insistently upon each other.

Jesus' disciples once saw the Lord with their own eyes and heard his voice with their own ears. In Jesus they experienced theology in the most literal, personal sense. They did not just study it in books or under professors. Thus John speaks for all the apostles and disciples when he says in his first epistle that all of them preached only what they had seen with their own eyes, heard with their own ears, and touched with their own hands; that is, what they had lived through as reality. The miracles belonged and belong to this reality. Jesus could perform them with his Father's help because he was not just a rabbi of written learning but a rabbi of nature as well. In the story of the creation (Genesis 1:26), the triune God says, "Let us make man in our image, after our likeness." Jesus is a participant in this deed. In the Old Testament, in Proverbs 30:4, these questions are asked: "Who has ascended into heaven and come down? Who has gathered the wind in his fists? Who has wrapped up the waters in a garment? Who has established all the ends of the earth? What is his name, and what is his son's name? Surely you know!" The favorite disciple was not conveying a pet idea that had originated with him when he wrote, in reference to the "Word," "All things were made through him, and without him was not anything made that was made." He was conveying a part of the elementary knowledge of the original congregation. Thirty years earlier Paul had proclaimed his knowledge of Jesus in Colossians 1:15-17 in the following words: "He is the image of the invisible God, the first-born of all creation; for in him all things were created, in heaven and on earth, visible and invisible . . .—all things were created through him and for him. He is before all things, and in him all things hold together." And elsewhere, in I Corinthians 8:6, Paul says "Yet for us there is one God, the Father, from whom are all things and for whom we exist, and one Lord, Jesus Christ, through whom are all things and through whom we exist."

The reader will find further evidence in the New Testament in John 1:3,10; Ephesians 3:9; Romans 11:36; Hebrews 1:2,10; Revelation 3:14 and 4:11.

In the foregoing I have not merely explained what I personally understand by theology; relying on the unambiguous words of the New Testament, I have also indicated that I look upon Jesus as the creator of the world and of nature, and hence of physics.[14] This faith and knowledge has largely disappeared today. That is why there is so much bewilderment when the subject of this book is raised. Nowadays most people are unaware that faith and science are not contradictions, but one and the same. Of course, when we sing the ninth verse of the Christmas carol "Vom Himmel hoch da komm ich her," we dutifully recite, "Oh, Lord, thou Creator of all things, how poor thou hast become"; but in neither this song nor in many others do we get the point.

Let us take another brief glance at the way theology is commonly understood. I shall limit myself to the use of the term in Christianity, for there is "orthodox," "liberal," "fundamentalist," "dialectic," "existentialist," "modernist," and every other possible form of theology. To my eyes these are all cases of using secularly colored and one-sided, if often well-intentioned, supplements to make the original, unadorned theology of the Bible more agreeable to oneself and other people. Sometimes such theology deviates but little from the teachings of the Bible; in those cases, it serves to educate and strengthen the congregation. But sometimes it deviates considerably. It then resembles "laboring for the wind," to repeat the phrase often used in Ecclesiastes. In this case one should speak of theologism rather than theology, for God's word is being mixed with existentialism, modernism, and the other "isms" of this world.

III. PHYSICS

The word "physics" is derived from the Greek word for nature. *Physis* is nature. Accordingly, I use the word "physics" in this book in the broad sense of "natural science." Natural science is divided into several fields in practice—astronomy, biology, geology, chemistry, physics in the narrow sense, etc. But physics narrowly defined provides the broadest laws, principles, and methods of measurement, and these are applicable to all other fields. It also makes the most intensive use of the specialized language of mathematics. Hence the word "physics" stands here for natural science as a whole. I shall mention biology as well as physics only when referring to life functions or lives that can be understood only through the syntheses of physics and biology.

The working methods of physics rest on just two pillars—experimentation and mathematics. (We can for the moment ignore the fact that the talent and intuition of a few scientists have more impact than the abilities of the majority of their colleagues working with mathematics and physics.) Experimentation, consisting of nature's answers and statements, takes priority. Not only must every mathematical computation be checked experimentally for validity and applicability, but changes and enlargements of our current ideas have been wrested only from experimentation. It can well be said that a good experiment is the best theory. Physical theories are expressed preferentially through mathematics. A good theory, to use Hermann von Helmholtz' phrase, is the most practical thing one can imagine. The function of mathematical physics may be described as that of polishing the raw diamonds removed by experimenters from the dark bowels of the earth until they shine and glitter like polished diamonds.

Experimentation and mathematics are extremely sharp and

immediately effective critics whenever a physicist begins to indulge in fantasy, speculation, or ideology in his work. Many theologians and members of Christian congregations fail to take that into account, for they think that physicists are guided in their research by philosophical considerations and ideological motivations. They believe that theories advanced by physicists are not only a reflection of that, but are a substitute religion as well. That a physicist may have philosophical, theological, and ideological motives cannot be denied, for he too is a child of his time and environment. But there is none of that in his experiments of mathematical formulas, for they contain nothing but the actual answers of nature. There have of course always been people who have sought an inadmissible mixture of physics, theology, philosophy, and even politics, hoping to make physics dependent upon the others. But there have seldom been great scientists among them, and science, except for slight, localized deviations, has never followed such tendencies.

A few examples should remind us that there is knowledge which, while experimentally and mathematically sound, leads to unfortunate consequences when combined with philosophy, theology, and politics:

1. The Bible was not an authoritative textbook of physics, theologically justifying the church's authority over Copernicus, Galileo, or Bruno. Treating it thus resulted in the destruction of confidence in the church.[18] It cannot be stated too often that the Bible, by its own statements in the first chapters of Genesis, must not be regarded as a textbook of physics or biology.[14]

2. Marxist philosophy seized control of natural science one hundred years ago, elevating materialism to a faith. No one is happier as a result. It has been recognized today that science has socio-political significance. Strangely enough, many people wish to subordinate it to an ideology, such as Marxism, as well.

3. Marxist-Leninist ideology argues that it alone makes possible great achievements in physics. The truth is that it cripples the scientists under its sway.

4. It is inadmissible to overestimate the great achievements of one's own people in physics and to discredit those of other people on political and racist grounds.

5. Finally, the worldwide practice of keeping physicists and physics secret for military reasons leads only to fear and enormous expense, not to progress and peace.

Upon close examination of the miracles reported in the Scriptures we find that theology and physics touch upon each other and overlap. This century's physics supplies us with knowledge and experimental results which, more than ever before, are in striking harmony with theology.[10,11] I am referring only to biblical theology, which takes the Bible's statements and witnesses seriously. Major contradictions arise, however, when one places unreasonable constructions, for which close examination would reveal no basis, on the biblical accounts.[14] Among these constructions are: the view that the days of the Creation were equivalent to ordinary calendar days; the view that the entire world was instantaneously created only about 7,000 years ago but that God built in an age-deception factor; and, finally, the contention that human nature as it now is no longer reflects creation of God, since it runs counter to Jesus' Sermon on the Mount. Yet the Sermon on the Mount is addressed not to animals and plants, but to people, specifically to those who are serious in their desire to be Christians and disciples. On the other hand, the modernistic theologies that hold sway today include the view that the story of the Creation, together with the Resurrection and all the other miracles of the Old and New Testaments, are myths—i.e., fables void of reality. In addition, the entire mode of speaking in the Bible is said to be highly mythological in tone, and therefore to require reinterpretation if it is to have any value in meeting the needs of so-called modern man. But modern physics challenges these "modern" theologies without stepping over the line between theology and physics.[8] It has the power to force such theologies to reflect on the value of the true biblical theology.

A reproach commonly addressed to me and my scientific colleagues who are in the service of Jesus is that, while such news is welcome, the research position of physics is constantly changing. Books and newspapers in the past have spoken only too often of "a revolution in physics." The view of the world[11] presented by nineteenth-century physics allegedly led to godless materialism. Though that physics has now been surmounted and physics in the twentieth century is moving in the opposite direction, it is not unlikely—some say—that physics in the twenty-first century will renew its support for materialism.[7]

To this I should like to say that physics as such simply cannot evolve backwards; nor has it done so in any century since Copernicus. The problem here is that political thought and experience are injected into physics. In politics, democracy alternates with dictatorship, revolution with reaction. Each time there is an upheaval, which all too often leads to a return of the old. That does not happen in physics. Through the growth of experimental evidence, the development of mathematical methods, and the expansion of the content of its most important theories, physics marches steadily in the direction of expanded knowledge. Accurate knowledge and the results of earlier research are *never* simply discarded; rather, they serve as building blocks for further advances. The celestial mechanics founded by Kepler, Galileo, and Newton are still valid today. Their victories are celebrated in the space programs. The theory of electricity taught by Volta, Örstedt, Faraday, and Maxwell is still valid today. It is the main foundation of our power industry. Darwin's principle of evolution still dominates biology where, since the discovery of the laws of heredity and the fact of mutation, it has proved itself to an extent that Darwin himself could hardly have expected.[5,14] The twentieth-century contributions—relativity theory, quantum physics, and molecular biology—will be fully as valid in the twenty-first. Results and knowledge have never been discarded merely to return to something older.

Certain overly absolute statements and overly narrow interpretations, which either confine or overextend the area to which physical laws apply, must be constantly rechecked and discarded. The adulteration of physics with ideological questions must in no case be tolerated. The most notorious example is the well-known book by Ernst Haeckel, who is otherwise a highly competent researcher. His catechism of materialism, *The Riddle of the Universe,* had just one goal—to challenge and destroy faith in Jesus Christ. But even if one considers that Haeckel merely overshot the mark in seeking to defend himself in regard to the atheistic thinking imputed to him, the fact remains that it is physics and not theology that has rendered untenable all theses that appeared usable against religion at the turn of the twentieth century.

Good physicists have one trait in common with biblical theologians—they both inquire of God when they wish to know something. When, through experimentation, they inquire of nature, they are inquiring of God, the Creator of nature. Logically, then, there is no court of appeal against an answer given by an experiment. Experimentation has definitively shown that affirmations on physics which the Bible does not make— such as the statement that the sun revolves around the earth— must not be imputed to the Bible. Experimentation has shown that ignorance of the achievements of physics and use of an outdated level of knowledge, on the basis of which many judgments cannot be made, are no grounds for declaring biblical miracles to be myths. It is a secularized theology—not biblical theology—that has had to succumb to the principle of evolution in the nineteenth century. It is only a secularized, existentialist theology that today regards the miracles as myths divorced from reality, and that for this purpose calls upon a form of the law of cause and effect that physics has long since put behind it.[14]

A few more comments on the concept of interpretation of nature are in order at this point. By interpretation of nature, including the physical aspect of miracles, I mean first of all the relating of new observations to phenomena that are already known and have already been mastered. A new phenomenon may be deemed adequately explained when it is incorporated into an existing system or structure.

It has often proved impossible, at least at first, to relate and incorporate new observations in this way. This was the case with the discoveries of electricity, superconductivity, particle waves, and the Mendelian laws of heredity. Among today's still totally unexplained phenomena are the problem of the divining rod, psychokinesis, and many biblical miracles. In the first-named cases, numerous experiments vouched for the discoveries, which scientists eventually were able to understand and incorporate into the then-known systems. When this was done, then, these phenomena in turn were available to help explain subsequent discoveries. All of our interpretive efforts really amount to nothing more than digesting new evidence, i.e, relating an X to a Y.

But difficulties arose even with this modest interpretation of nature when we discovered atoms as physical realities and learned, in addition, that all matter is a statistical combination of atomic structures. As we shall indicate in chapter 7, we thereby reached a knowledge barrier that prevents us from using the type of picture, drawn from macroscopic observation, that is usual in interpretation of this kind, and, in particular, from adhering to the law of cause and effect in its old form. Hence we must now give up even the relatively modest concept of interpretation described above. We are beginning to speak of describing nature rather than of interpreting it. If we succeed in developing workable mathematical forms for such description, we have gone far. Waiving deeper interpretation does not reduce our ability to achieve the best possible grasp of nature.

IV. MIRACLES

1. THE CONCEPT OF MIRACLES[13]

Now that we have given a few illustrations in the areas of theology and physics, we shall give a few on the concept of miracles.

What is a miracle? Sometimes, to the extent that friend and foe agree, it appears that an unambiguous answer can be given. In general, however, they do not agree—particularly when one group denies the existence and even the possibility of miracles, and the other personally experiences them and derives strength from them. Obviously, the personality of the experiencer, the one spoken to, or—to put it most generally—the participant, is all too often incorporated into the precise definition of the miracle. Therefore, a miracle is often not objectifiable or repeatable by anyone at any time in any place. It may, however, lend itself to being experienced and observed though, on principle, not at a time and place of our choosing.

Scientists above all have a natural approach to the question of miracles. Ultimately, the way they differ from other people is that, for professional reasons, they have and seek better relations with nature. If an event or phenomenon falls outside the framework of the commonplace or the normal and never or only seldom recurs, they can experience the miracle more consciously in its simplest form. Their curiosity comes to the fore, and they ask, "Why is this so?" Curiosity leads to research, thence to the discovery of the how and why, and finally to an explanation. But even the finest explanation leaves intact a humble man's amazement and quiet worship. If no explanation—i.e., no relating to previously known facts—is possible, the discovery is profoundly new, can be made familiar through constant repetition and description, and only then initiates one to genuine wonderment.

All the biblical miracles have in common the fact that they depart from the commonplace. This is true not only of their outward form but of the time of their occurrence. The outward form of many miracles can be explained in physical terms, while the time of their occurrence cannot be so explained, being understandable only in terms of the biblical story of the life and sufferings of Christ. In not a few cases the outward form is of little physical interest; the miracle lies in the time of its occurrence and in the prayer that motivated or actuated it.

2. VARIETIES OF MIRACLES

In my book *Jesus, Master of Nature* I distinguish four groups of miracles so that they can be discussed in a more orderly way.[14] Occasionally a miracle falls into two different groups.

The first group consists of miracles experienced even today by persons called by the Lord and by many believing Christians. These are for the most part internal experiences. The Bible often describes them in the sentence, "The word of the Lord came to . . ." On occasion an external sign apprises the recipient that God is about to say something to him, either as a reprimand or answering of a prayer intended for him personally or as an instruction to be carried out for or against other people or powers. Anyone can experience this, for example, in reading the Bible or the daily text or in listening carefully to a sermon. How often the texts of the Moravians have given me just the direction I needed, and with it inner strength and comfort! The causes of revival movements always lie in such miracles. Here we can experience the way in which God hears us and answers us—though of course only if we ourselves are ready to hear him *first*. Here sinners receive communion with God. This really comes as a shock. We see examples of it in the Jesus-People movements. We can see just how genuine and amazing these examples are from the fact that the Devil has mobilized all his children on the editorial staffs of the yellow press to exploit rock operas, Jesus Christ

Superstar figures, Jesus trips, "religious" ballets, and the like for financial purposes while ridiculing the conversion of sinners.

The miracles of this first group do not really fit our title, *Theology, Physics, and Miracles.* Physics has little to say about them. Yet they play a major, if not the decisive, role in the daily life of Christian believers. They supply that certainty of the presence of Jesus in the Holy Spirit which vouches for the credibility and reality of all the other miracles recorded in the Bible, without requiring anyone to have a deep knowledge of physics. I myself gained the strength to preach this, as I do in this book and in the book with the significant title *Jesus, Master of Nature,* not from research in physics, but from the miracles with which the Lord spoke to me in the Bible, through the apostolic preaching of his devoted ministers, and through the Holy Spirit.

A young man recently reproached me for basing my theology and my lectures on the conviction that God exists. It was his view that God does not exist, and that our God merely provides a sort of stop-gap explanation for relationships and feelings that we do not adequately understand. My reply was to ask whether I myself could legitimately base my presentation on the presupposition that God does not exist. I experience him as reality. In the language of technology, I have a direct connection to Jesus. I am not expected to prove God through physics or other means, but only, as Jesus wanted, to bear witness to him. Hence, I only ask that each honest doubter carry out an experiment; discover for yourself, through study of the Bible, whether it consists merely of the thoughts of men, or whether, through the Holy Spirit, Jesus speaks to us in those thoughts.

The second group of miracles recorded in the Bible consists of unusual, remarkable events in inanimate nature. They remain miracles even if we have no difficulty explaining them or can occasionally observe them again, since the time of occurrence, as I indicated above, is almost more miraculous than the event itself. A few of the many accounts that belong in this category are Moses and the burning bush, the crossing of the Red Sea, the trumpets of Jericho, the sun standing still at Gibeon, the dew on the fleece put out by Gideon, the conversion of water to wine at the wedding in Cana, Peter's miraculous catch on the Sea of Galilee, the coin in the fish's mouth, the darkness when Jesus died. I have discussed miracles of this type in detail in my German book "Christ and Research in Physics."[13]

For over a century, "modern" theologians have excelled at ridiculing anyone who takes these accounts seriously. For decades I have longed to see just one scientific treatise by such a theologian using the methods of physical science in an effort to prove the untenability of these accounts. The chances are that I shall wait in vain.

The third group of miracles has to do with medical events. It is closely related to psychology and to parapsychology, which stands so undeservedly in ill repute.[3] In these miracles, lame, deaf, blind people, and lepers are healed; the motive power of spiritual forces, transmitted to others and acting at a distance, is also involved. We learn from Jesus' works what is possible. In the fourteenth chapter of his Gospel, John conveys these challenging words of Jesus, which beckon us to natural science and which I as a physicist find fascinating: "He who believes in me will also do the works that I do; and greater works than these will he do." Jesus' miracles are among his works. It is depressing to see how negatively some people who fancy themselves to be devout react when anyone, pursuant to these words of Jesus, performs wonders with the sick. They raise a great clamor and complain of occultism, though nothing more is involved than the methods of depth psychology, psychiatry, and autogenous training. Scientific parapsychology, which today is forced to limit itself to painfully precise stocktaking and recording[3] and which is represented in Germany by Professor Bender, is similarly condemned without mercy as occultism.

We must of course not forget that the pious Pharisees ac-

cused Jesus of driving out the demons in the course of his healings with the help of the Devil (Matthew 9:34; 12:24 ff.).
Responding that, in that case, Satan was destroying his own
kingdom, Jesus continued his miraculous healings. In the
statement quoted above, he invites us to work as he works,
which we can do through assiduous, honest study. Research in
parapsychology on the spiritual forces unknown to physics,[3]
now in its initial stages, can no more be stopped than could
celestial mechanics, the theory of electricity, the principle of
evolution in biology, or quantum mechanics be stopped today.

The fourth group of miracles, being linked much more
closely than the others to the person of Jesus, is a component
of the credos to which all Christianity adheres—the Apostles'
Creed, the Nicene Creed, and the Athanasian Creed. The
Apostles' Creed is the best known, while the Nicene is the
most precise. We shall return later to the Athanasian Creed,
which depicts the trinity of God. The credos deal with the
Resurrection, the Ascension, and the effusion of the Holy Spirit.
Also in the fourth group are the accounts of the Virgin Birth,
the raising of Jairus' daughter and the youth at Nain, and
the bringing of Lazarus back from the grave, as well as the
events on the mount of the transfiguration. Though Christians
may differ or be reticent in their attitudes toward the miracles
in the second and third groups, their position on the fourth
group determines whether they believe in the triune God or
have merely accepted a modern theological "ism." It cannot be
proclaimed loudly enough that those central events that the
creeds proclaim actually occurred. If they did not, as Paul
says, we would be the most miserable deceivers and self-deceivers (cf. I Corinthians 15:12-20). But the experience of
miracles in the first group is a step toward the certainty that
the miracles in the fourth group are real. The theologian Hermann v. Bezzel, former President of the Bavarian Evangelical
Church, has pointed out in his thoughtful book *God's Servant
(Der Knecht Gottes)* that there is a unique miracle which cannot be placed in any other category of miracles. This miracle is

Jesus. As the Son of God, he did not come to dwell *near* us, so that he could later strike his tent and move on, in the manner of an exalted prince. Rather, he came to dwell *among* us, as John testifies in the fourteenth verse of the first chapter of his Gospel. He remained among humans for a considerable time. Though the Son of God, he was so human in his development, his bearing, and his bodily needs, that the miracle in him was precisely the fact that there was nothing miraculous about him. God's love manifested itself in him in quite a natural manner, on a creaturely level, not in a mystical, metaphysical way that eluded comprehension.

3. THE LANGUAGE OF MIRACLES

Most "modern" theologians regard the miracles as myths, i.e., as implausible, virtually fantastic accounts. They hold that these myth-miracles originated in the culture of the ancient Israelite communities and in the mythological conceptions of early Christian congregations. Consequently, they contend that physical realities cannot and should not be attached to these mythological conceptions. But I find over and over again that these theologians never even entertain the humble thought that some miracles may be credible at least in physical terms and may therefore deserve thoughtful consideration. It is not surprising, then, that besides classifying the events and accounts as myths, they regard the unique, wondrous language of the biblical text at decisive points as mythological, illogical, ambiguous, and derived from a long-outdated view of the world.

Just as the experimental findings are imbedded in a good theory of physics, and the two are inseparable, so the miracles are imbedded in the distinctive miracle-language of the Bible, inspired by the Holy Spirit, and the language is inseparable from the miracles. The analogy is somewhat defective, because biblical discourse, infused with the Spirit, is something perfect, while a human theory is something limited. I hope, however, that the reader will understand what I mean. In view of the great importance of this connection, I should like to categorize the wondrous language among the miracles, and specifically among the first group. God used it in speaking to the prophets and apostles, who passed it on to the congregations and their pastors, who return it to God in prayer and worship (Isaiah 55:11). Examples will be given shortly. We shall return to some of them in a later chapter.

Theology is a language or discourse of the miraculous, as we defined it above, for it links the person of God with the state that is the Holy Spirit, calling them identical in substance and inseparable. The Holy Spirit appears now as a person acting concretely, now as a spiritual state that fills a congregation. Jesus stands before the disciples and says, *"I am . . .* the truth" (John 14:6); but, again, he says to us, "Every one who is of the truth hears my voice" (John 18:37). Jesus not only says, *"I am* the resurrection and the life" (John 11:25), but also, "I *will* raise him up *at the last day"* (John 6:40). It is wondrous language that says, "The wages of sin is death," thus establishing a causal connection between a biological fact and the spiritual position of man.[14]

V. DOUBLE NEGATION

In Numbers 23:12 we read, "Must I not take heed to speak what the Lord puts in my mouth?" But the refusal by friends and members of the congregation to do so places some of the Lord's servants in a situation described as follows by Jeremiah (Jeremiah 20:9): "If I say, 'I will not mention him [that is, the Lord], or speak any more in his name,' there is in my heart as it were a burning fire shut up in my bones, and I am weary with holding it in, and I cannot." I sometimes have the same resolve, and yet I am compelled to follow unswervingly the instruction of the Apostle Peter (I Peter 4:10): "As each has received a gift, employ it for one another."

In performing this service, however, one is often misunderstood, both by people who consider themselves believers in the Bible but have an aversion to physics, and by people who simply cannot accept that a physicist would believe wholeheartedly in Jesus. The former complain of scientific desecration of the Word of God, while the latter turn relevant statements of the author upside down and insist that people be warned emphatically against borrowing his books.

In my statements I *never* seek to prove that, as the saying goes, "the Bible is right after all," or that *all* miracles will sooner or later be explicable. I am far more concerned with exposing those who with so much self-assurance categorize the miracles as myths or physical impossibilities, proclaim the Bible's alleged view of the world to be outdated, and then support their contentions with a materialistic world view that has long been regarded as obsolete by physicists.[11] They of course fail to point out that even in the heyday of naturalism many great physicists rejected materialistic world views in any form.[13]

24

On Pentecost in 1962, the late theologian Otto Weber, a professor of reformed theology at Göttingen, presented a paper on the status of theology. Walter Stöcker, who chaired the meeting at Dassel, had requested that he do so. He delivered the paper while still freshly impressed by a conference of theologians at Göttingen, held under the chairmanship of the well-known demythologizer Bultmann, with renowned physicists in attendance. Before giving any particulars on the content of the discussion, Weber summarized the situation as follows: "I must say how humiliating it was. Physicists sat there declaring their faith, and theologians sat there denying theirs." I took down some of what Weber said. Subjects discussed in this book, such as the problem of causality, were discussed at the conference. In the course of the discussion, Weber reported, one of the physicists said to Professor Bultmann that it was not right that he and other professors tell their students nothing more about physics than what they had learned sixty years earlier from their school teachers. Physics has changed considerably since then, and the physicists in attendance wished to observe in all humility that they had had more than a little to do with bringing the changes about. I have been citing the theologian Weber. In his book *Creation and Mystery*,[8] the physicist P. Jordan argues that all of Bultmann's efforts were based on the unalterable conviction that science today is just where it was one hundred years ago, and that errors stemming from the status of the sciences at that time must still be respectfully accepted by theology as irrefutable truths superior to theology.

When the theologian Weber stated in his report that the physicists declared their faith while the theologians denied theirs, he did not mean that the physicists had recognized Jesus Christ as their Saviour or that the theologians had presented themselves as atheists. He was referring, rather, to the subject of the discussion—the law of causality which was inherent in the old world view and which has been replaced today by another causality principle. The anti-religious conclusions drawn in the past from the law in its old form, as well as all conclusions relegating miracles to the category of mere myths, are wrong. Physics has developed in such a way that it negates all turn-of-the-century world views—hailed by many people as achievements—which arrogantly claimed to negate the biblical stories totally. This *double negation*, which Professor Jordan, as far as I know, was the first to point out,[7,8] is precisely the point. It has made many physicists more alert and careful, so that they now refuse to involve themselves in the contesting of biblical stories.

By examining certain miracles, we can gain greater insight into the essence of creation. We also anticipate that astounding things will come of the knowledge to be referred to in chapter 7 below. But at the same time we recognize our limits. As regards the central facts of Christianity—the cross, forgiveness of sins, and the Resurrection—every Christian, nay, every human being, must make his own personal religious decision in our day, just as at all times in the past. The double negation offers no proof of God; it merely disproves the alleged proofs from the past that God does not exist. Before the Saviour of sinners, the scholarly physicist enjoys no advantage over the poor day laborer.

VI. THE CONFORMITY OF MIRACLES TO THE LAWS OF NATURE [13, 14]

In the very first chapter of the Bible I find three crucial theological propositions. The first is contained in the twenty-seventh verse, which reads: "God created man in his own image, in the image of God he created him; male and female he created them." In other words, man was literally created in such a manner that he bears the likeness of Jesus in himself.[14] The second fundamental proposition is in verse 28, which reads: "Be fruitful and multiply, and fill the earth and subdue it; and have dominion over the fish of the sea and over the birds of the air and over every living thing that moves upon the earth." This proposition assigns a number of tasks to mankind. Through inquiry he is to be God's housekeeper and master of the world. That means, too, that he can learn to interpret and understand the miracles in physical terms. The third proposition is in verse 31, which says: "And God saw everything that he had made, and behold, it was very good." Let us examine this proposition more closely, for it contains a fundamental statement of theology.

The comment that the things brought into existence by God's word are "good" appears seven times in Genesis. But at the end of the act of creation itself, God says of them that they are "very good." In other words, God *never* rescinds his own natural laws, which constitute and maintain his creation. That which he calls "very good," he does not later treat as inadequate. Since, in view of the trinity of God, we may with equal validity say that Jesus characterized his creation as "very good," all the miracles of the Old and New Testaments, including the Resurrection, are consistent with the natural laws of creation. Augustine, a father of the church, made this point when he said that the miracles clash not with nature, but merely with the natural laws thus far known to us. He was of course referring to the knowledge of nature in his own time. But, though we know today that many miracles do not "clash" with nature, Augustine's judgment is still applicable to others.

Moreover, it is a physical impossibility to prove that miracles recorded in the Bible clash with nature. To prove that with precision, one would need a *total* knowledge of all the laws of nature. It is certain that we do not now and never shall possess such knowledge. Though we may achieve a breakthrough in the level of our knowledge of nature at any given time, we can never pierce nature itself. Augustine expressed the situation clearly and soberly. Mankind would have been spared much pain if the church had taken Augustine's perception to heart. By adhering instead to a dogma on scientific advances that had no biblical justification, and by imputing incomprehensible occurrences of a medical or physical nature to sorcerers, demons, and devils, the church incurred guilt for many horrors, especially witchhunts, the Inquisition, and the persecution of Galileo and Bruno. It did infinitely more harm to its credibility in this way than that done by theoretical theological disputes.

Human thoughtlessness sometimes causes otherwise discerning Christians even today to say that God can help his congregations in need only by rescinding his natural laws. God has thousands upon thousands of possibilities for helping people that we with our limited knowledge of nature cannot imagine. Jesus' statement that he would not set aside so much as a tittle of the Law may properly be understood to mean as well that he does not set aside so much as a tittle of natural law, but rather carries it out fully. The natural laws are the content of creation, which is part of the "law," or Torah, of the ancient Jews. To me personally, the third fundamental proposition in Genesis is plainly the *crucial point* in discussing the interrelationship of theology and physics and the relationship of both to biblical miracles.

It is providential that we are explicitly told on the very first page of the Bible that the natural laws of creation, which underlie the miracles, are "very good" and hence above criticism.

But I also perceive it as providential that the physics of our time provides us with deeper insights than ever before into the essence of creation. In this regard we can say with Paul (I Corinthians 2:10): "The Spirit searches everything, even the depths of God."

It is painful to note that many active churchgoers, though they name themselves after Jesus Christ, refuse to recognize God's and Jesus' judgment that the creation is "very good." They say to me time after time: "God is all-powerful. Why shouldn't he be able to set natural laws aside when he wishes to perform a miracle?" My answer is that God can do anything he wants, but that he doesn't. He is a *faithful* God, not fickle in what he says. Thus, in Numbers 23:19 the following questions appear: "Has he said, and will he not do it? Or has he spoken, and will he not fulfill it?" If God said that creation is very good, he never treats it as inadequate. In any case I trust his faithfulness. On the basis of many years' experience, I cannot rid myself of the impression that people who insist that God sets his natural laws aside harbor deep doubts in their hearts about the extent of God's power. This impression is reinforced by their readiness to follow preachers who, though they have made little attempt to probe into physics, trumpet their false scientific notions to Christian congregations.

At the same time there are important scientists who have no concept of a personal God and who know little about Jesus; yet they not only acknowledge the third basic theological proposition of Genesis but also treat it as a definition of the essence of God. They identify the "very good" of natural law with God himself.

We shall return to the question of consonance with natural law in section 9 of chapter 7. We must first see how Genesis 1:31 may have been affected by the fall of man.

In basing my entire theological work as a physicist on the seven "goods" and final judgment "very good" in Genesis, I have based it on a biblical rather than a scientific proposition. I do not venture, however, to interpret "good" or "very good" as "perfect." I have repeatedly observed that such an interpretation is made only in order to be able to say afterward that the entire creation had become imperfect when man fell, was more likely the work of Satan than the work of God, and was in need of redemption. Such thinking leads to one conflict after another between faith and science. Modernistic theologies flourish on these artificial conflicts. From my point of view the judgments "good" and "very good" contain Jesus' urgent admonition that we avoid negative verdicts on creation, reflected in the tendency of some of us to believe that God in his miracles repeatedly ignores his laws of creation, and the tendency of others to say that all the miracles, including the Resurrection, are only man-made myths.[14]

At this point, I shall cite but one example of these false verdicts on creation: It is said that since, according to chapters 11 and 65 of Isaiah, the lion shall one day eat straw, the lion's present way of life must be opposed to God. But nothing of the sort is meant here. Let us be guided by Psalm 104, which glorifies God for the works of his creation. Verses 20 and 21 read: "Thou makest darkness and it is night, when all the beasts of the forest creep forth. The young lions roar for their prey, seeking their food *from God.*"

VII. DISCOVERIES IN PHYSICS EVALUATED THEOLOGICALLY

1. INTRODUCTION

We must necessarily limit ourselves to outlining results and knowledge obtained by physics[1,2,4,6] which have caused people to be more hesitant in criticizing biblical miracles and speech and to take biblical stories far more seriously than contemporary theology is wont to do. I shall attempt to show how the new knowledge rests on the solid foundation of the old and leads us to questions and statements that would once have been classified as theological and cast aside.

After the next section, which deals with space and time, all the sections will deal almost exclusively with atoms. Everyone has heard of atoms since Otto Hahn succeeded in splitting the atomic nucleus of uranium, ultimately confronting mankind with the most frightful possibilities. The existence of atoms can no longer be doubted. There is something sinister about their reality, not just because of the Bomb,[9] but also because of the limits they place on our knowledge. Around the year 1900, many truly significant and worthy physicists still denied the existence of atoms as physical bodies with structures, viewing them instead as mental images or helpful hypotheses. There is perhaps deep logic in the fact that those who most sharply rejected the atomic concept were leading materialists. But, as we know today, the year 1900 was a turning point in physics. It was then that Max Planck made his discoveries—so insignificant in the layman's eyes—on quanta of energy in light and heat radiation. Theologians whose emphasis on mythicizing and existentialism makes them masters of the present still refuse to recognize this turning point.

31

2. THE RELATIVITY OF SPACE AND TIME[7,13]

It is often said, or at least so understood by laymen, that Einstein's theory of relativity replaced the celestial mechanics begun by Copernicus, Kepler, and Galileo, raised to its pinnacle by Newton, and extended mathematically by Laplace, Euler, d'Alembert, Hamilton, and others. Many assume that the relativity of every phenomenon has been substituted for concepts once accepted as absolute. There is even a popular saying that everything in the world is relative, by which is meant that there is no definitive yardstick in politics, morals, or social problems. But physics, here represented by the theory of relativity, lends no support to such a view.

The old formulas for computing and following the positions and movements of all types of heavenly bodies (stars, planets, moons, comets) are just as valid today as ever. The computers that track satellites and spacecraft are also governed by those same formulas. *Only* when the speed of moving bodies approaches that of light—which is not usually the case—does the old system need to be supplemented. As before, the paths and curves of movement are relative to each other and are therefore described differently by different observers; but, in addition, length, mass, and time now become relative, i.e., dependent upon the state of motion. To express this in concrete terms, the mass of a body grows as its speed approaches that of light, rather than remaining constant, as had previously been thought. A watch that tells the time slows down as the vehicle nears the velocity of light. This is not apparent to a traveler within the vehicle, but only by comparison with a watch outside it. Thus, mass and time have become relative. Contrary to earlier belief, time does not pass "eternally and changelessly."

The fact that relativity is measured against the velocity of light in empty space is of decisive importance. That velocity is enormous—some 186,000 miles per second. The speed of light is accepted as the absolute constant in the theory of relativity, not because human beings in their wisdom so desired, but because carefully prepared experiments so indicated. (The best known experiment was that performed in 1887 in Cleveland by Albert Abraham Michelson with his light interferometer.) The mathematical formulas for describing the relativity of space, time, and mass with precision all contain the relationship of a body's velocity to the absolute constant of the speed of light in a vacuum. Thus, the theory of relativity could just as well be called the theory of the absolute. Since the heavenly bodies move slowly in relation to the speed of light, relativity of space, time, and mass is negligible in their case. That applies fully to our daily lives. But relativity is quite perceptible in machines that split atomic nuclei, for they accelerate electrical particles to a speed approaching that of light.

Now let us look again at the popular proposition that everything in life is relative and at the view of many laymen that the theory of relativity has made that proposition fully applicable in physics as well. It is generally overlooked by such persons that in actuality everything in physics is measured against the absolute constant which is the speed of light. But the popular proposition can and should have no validity for devout Christians, either. The Christian is, after all, in possession of an absolute value—the Word of God, as attested by the Holy Spirit and as taught by Jesus. All things should be measured against that value. Naturally, this offends the world out there, which would be forced to give up so many things dear to it. Many things in daily life truly are of relative value; among them are political structure, educational systems, church constitutions, and economic structures. But other things, such as the content of sermons, criminal law, and matters of marriage and sex, must be measured against the absolute word of Jesus. The public treatment of such matters as the latter demonstrates that secular relativity is extremely popular today, while the absolute Word of God is not in great demand.

In the nature of things, most research on space, time, and matter does not take place within the four walls of a laboratory. Since its purpose is to extend and refine old knowledge of celestial mechanics, it must be applicable everywhere. Immediate efforts to determine the consequences of the new insights for the structure of the universe were therefore inevitable. A fascinated curiosity about the nature of the starry heavens is as old as man himself, or goes at least as far back as the written records take us. It is not surprising that the Old Testament in Genesis and the New Testament in the story of the Magi's travels open with cosmic statements, and that the New Testament ends with such statements as well.

Thus, the problem of the starry heavens was as urgent to physicists a little over half a century ago as it had been 400 years earlier in the time of Copernicus.[7] A new branch of learning—the study of the origin and structure of the universe—came into being at that time. This development was introduced by two scientific works, one by Einstein and one by de Sitter. Einstein attacked the old question of whether the amount of star matter in space is infinite or merely finite and of how extensive the universe is. Einstein came to the conclusion that the universe is of only finite size and contains a finite amount of matter, but that it is otherwise limitless. This means that it cannot be described in just three-dimensional terms (length, width, height), but that a fourth dimension, which we cannot concretely picture, must be added. A layman can best understand the concept "finite and yet limitless" by thinking of a globe that represents the earth. We humans live on the surface of the earth. The surface is finite, for we know that it has an area of so many square miles. But at the same time it is limitless. Wherever we travel on the earth's surface, we never reach a point where it ends. We must transfer this concept to the universe. Wherever we may let our thoughts take us, riding a ray of light, we never reach a point at which "the world stops." We end up back at our starting point, just as we do on earth if we are careful to move in the same direction at all times. And yet the universe is finite, for we can state its diameter and the amount of matter it contains.

De Sitter's work was based on the same premises as Einstein's, except that de Sitter assumed in addition that the matter in the universe is spreading outward in all directions, rather than being statically distributed. In 1929, using the giant telescope on Mount Palomar, Hubble made the decisive discovery that all spiral nebula—worlds like our Milky Way— are moving away from us, and with increasing velocity as their distance increases. That means, if one looks backward in time, that the entire system of spiral nebula and the stars they contain must have begun in a very small space. This "beginning of the world" occurred at least ten billion years ago. Measurements made since then on radioactive minerals and on meteorites, which are somewhat younger, fit in well with this estimate.

Of all these discoveries, that on the "beginning of the world" was the most fascinating, for it was not merely a thought expressed mathematically but nature's answer to experiments conducted with telescopes. Reminiscing at one point in his book on the theory of relativity, Max Born declares, "The idea of a 'beginning of the world' was so alien to scientists that some sought to avoid it by replacing it with a static concept." We must not forget that the view of existing matter as indestructible and changeless held sway at the turn of this century, for the physics of the atomic nucleus, in which a material particle can distintegrate in radiation and radiation can become matter, still lay in the future. The articles of the materialist faith, and the view of materialists that the biblical idea of a beginning of the world merited scorn and ridicule, were based on the state of knowledge at that time. If there had actually been a beginning of the world, the notion that time was eternal would suffer a death blow. What is more, the demand for a Creator-God would be unavoidable. But since Hubble's measurements, if not earlier, an assertion of the Bible, previously considered theological or mythological, has been a subject of research in physics.

Interestingly enough, the notion of the universe beginning in a small space and of a concomitant beginning of time leads one to infer that matter could have come into being out of nothing. In that case, one is again involved with a theological proposition. The first sentence of Genesis, as we know, reads, "In the beginning God created the heavens and the earth." Theology teaches us that the Hebrew word *bara* (to create) refers preferentially to creation out of nothing by God. But just what does "nothing" mean? It is not conceivable in the abstract. It is a relative concept. It can be defined only in relation to something. "Nothing" may be understood as the total absence of order and natural law in a primitive cluster of matter. But it may also be understood to mean that this world did not yet exist. And yet, there already was something there— the Word, i.e., Jesus. As far as can be determined from the present state of scientific knowledge, there was a beginning, which took place as matter began to expand from a very small space. This is also when time began. The early church father Augustine recognized this, for he writes in *The City of God*: "The world was without doubt created not *in* time, but *with* time. Before the world began, time could not have existed, for there was no creature through whose periodic movement it could have originated." Our present concept is that the beginning took place in the form of a "primeval explosion." The splitting asunder of primeval matter gave rise to extremely hot electromagnetic radiation, which gradually "cooled" with time, until it is now in the range of short electric waves. Experimentally derived evidence of this radiation in space has provided further support for the concept of a beginning of time, space, and matter.

It cannot be the purpose of this book, let alone of physical research, to provide evidence in support of the Bible or theology. Let us recall the aforementioned *double negation*. At the turn of the century the status of knowledge was as follows:

Universe of infinite size; matter in the universe infinite and indestructible; space and time absolute, eternal, and independent of matter; no beginning and no end.

The situation today is different: universe of finite size, but limitless; matter finite in quantity and may disintegrate into radiation; space and spatial structure dependent on matter; time relative and dependent on motion of matter; matter, space, and time had a beginning.

This world view offered by physics today is a negation of its predecessor. Concomitantly, it negates all the conclusions about the Bible which men thought they could draw from the earlier world view. The double negation rules out any misuse of physics in theological matters. But scholarly candor prevents us from stating baldly that the outdated world picture was fundamentally false. On the contrary, it is still valid within the bounds in which the relativity of space, time, and matter is negligible.

None of the explanations in this chapter on the relativity of space and time affects the miracles depicted in the Old or New Testament, unless one attempts to explain certain miracles, or at least to make them understandable, by introducing the fourth dimension in physics. I personally see no urgent grounds for doing so today. But the explanations in this chapter are probably consistent with biblical concepts and modes of speech regarding creation, beginning, and time. Physics has erected some caution signs. He who mocks even small sections of the Bible soon falls into rejection of all the rest.

3. ENERGY QUANTA

The old proposition, referred to above, that matter is indestructible, was replaced in 1905 by the concept of the equivalence of mass and energy. Mass is nothing more than clustered energy, in this view. Hasenöhrl was the first to formulate the concept; Einstein gave it its definitive expression.

The concept "energy" was not expressed precisely enough to be useful until the nineteenth century. Energy is the capacity of a body to do work. This definition gives the layman a feeling of what is meant by energy. In daily life, when we use steam engines, automobiles, airplanes, heating pads, refrigerators, and coke furnaces, it makes little difference whether energy is something continuous in space or whether it occurs in minute portions. In 1900, however, Planck discovered, in studying the radiation emanating from a heated body, that the energy in that radiation occurs in tiny portions. He called them energy elements, and we call them nowadays quanta of energy. The energy of such a quantum has the value $E = h \cdot v$, with v the frequency of the radiation and h an absolute constant in nature, known as Planck's constant. Thus, h has a significance as fundamental as that of the speed of light. Its value is extremely small; a quantum of energy in green light, for example, is only one-ten billionth of a billionth of a calorie. Hence, in the physics of daily life, also known as the macrocosm, we of course have no perception of discrete quanta of energy. In the microcosm, however, energy quanta play the role of heavy artillery for minute atoms, which are about one-ten millionth of a centimeter in diameter, and for their still smaller components, such as electrons. Here again we see that modern physics has merely refined and expanded our knowledge of energy, enabling us to apply that knowledge more meaningfully to atoms.

If mass is nothing more than a cluster of energy, that applies to the mass of an individual atom as well. If the energy content of an atom changes as the result of some physical process, the change can manifest itself only through discrete energy quanta. At least one quantum is operating. Another way of saying it is that the energy content has changed by at least one discrete quantum jump.

4. THE ORIGIN AND EFFECT OF LIGHT

Planck's discovery endowed an old concept of Newton's, dating from about 1700, with new meaning. Newton was of the opinion that light consists of minute particles speeding away from a shining body and received by the eye. But he could not advance a detailed opinion on the subject, since the state of physics at the time could offer him no knowledge on the actual points of emission or reception of light. After Newton, physicists concerned themselves with the qualities of light that could be studied in the area between the light source and the point of reception. Through these studies they learned that light is a wave motion, with qualities that can best be described by comparison with waves of water. A wave of water is created by a stone thrown into a pond. The wave itself is formed by the alternating rise and fall of the water. The distance between two elevations or between two depressions is called the wavelength. The number of times an elevation and a depression occur at a given point in a second is called the frequency. Light consists of an analogous process in space. It used to be thought that space was filled with ether. This notion was totally discarded when repeated efforts failed to turn up any evidence in support of it. The condition in space where light is present is described simply by what can be measured there, and that is the strength of the (electromagnetic) field of the light and its wavelength. Thus, light is no longer explained as waves in ether; one merely gives a description of what is measurable.

A major discovery was the finding that light is not just what our eye perceives, but also the electrical waves discovered by Heinrich Hertz, the rays discovered by Röntgen, and the gamma rays observed during atomic decay by Bequerel and Curie. In all these types of radiation, energy in the form of quanta is operating. Our eye, however, tells us only of those waves that we call visible light.

How does light, in the broad definition just outlined, come into being? A good, clear answer can be given on the basis of Heinrich Hertz's experiments, and the schools go into this at length. Örstedt and Ampère had discovered that a magnetic field, which deflects a magnetic needle, forms around an electrical current (in an electrical field). An electrical current is defined as moving electrical charges. Faraday subsequently found that an electrical field forms around a magnetic field whose strength changes, and that an electrical current results. Combining these discoveries with mathematical precision, Maxwell developed the following theory: when the strength of an electric current changes, a similarly changing magnetic field forms around it. An electrical field forms around that magnetic field, a magnetic field forms around this electrical field, then another electrical field, etc. Thus, an electromagnetic field spreads out in space, carrying energy. Hertz translated this theory into experimental reality. His varying electrical current consisted of oscillating electrons in metal wires which we call antennas today. The electrical waves emitted in this manner spread into space with the speed of ordinary light.

When the motion of free-flying high-speed electrons is modified by sudden deceleration, electrical waves are also formed, but their wavelength is much smaller. They are named Röntgen (or X-) rays for their discoverer. Finally, the electrical waves perceived by the human eye, which are called "light" in the more narrow, original sense of the word, also result from periodically oscillating or decelerated electrical charges, chiefly electrons.

This is not the place to present the multiple ways in which light can originate. We shall limit our comments to a single manner of origin, one which is of fundamental significance to our knowledge. After Lenard's discovery of the photoelectric effect, Einstein was able to explain it by recourse to Planck's discovery of quanta of energy. It was shown that a single electron was interacting with a single energy quantum of light, called a photon for short, within the atom to produce this effect. The electron would absorb the energy of the photon, thus increasing its own kinetic energy, and leave the atom. Niels Bohr later found that electrons, located in strictly preset areas of the atom shell, merely jump to areas farther away from the center when they absorb energy quanta; they leave the atom entirely only when they absorb the relatively large amount of energy required to do so. Of course the opposite can also occur; that is, an electron can jump from an outer to an inner orbit in which a vacancy has occurred. In so doing, the electron must surrender some energy in the form of a photon.

According to Bohr, light is produced in these cases by the jumping of electrons from energy-richer to energy-poorer areas of an atom. Stating it in terms more commonly used in daily life, the electrons move from a higher to a lower level. We might also say that light, in the form of photons of the most diverse sizes—recognizable by their color (i.e., frequency)—occurs when regrouping takes place in an atom. Since all matter consists of atoms, a macroscopic body such as a star can shine not only when moving electrical charges with it are decelerated but also when reorganizations occur in its atoms. If the order within the atoms is totally destroyed, with high temperatures causing them to collide at such speeds that they shatter each other and that order cannot be restored between the atomic nuclei and their electrons, the result is called *chaos* in Greek and *Tohuwabohu* in Hebrew. Light cannot be produced in this chaos by changes in the state of the atoms. If darkness is to be total, all the other manners of origin of light that were outlined above must also be absent. The motion of electrical charges must be severely limited. Such conditions are possible, and they are the subject of interesting debates among physicists.

Certain statements in Genesis now suddenly become physically understandable. According to Genesis, in the beginning there was chaos. The Word of God brought order to this chaos, and so there was light. In terms of the world as perceived by the biblical writer, we need consider only that light which is perceptible to the eye. It was not until much later, when gravitation caused shining matter to cluster together, that a sun came into being. The production of light is a primary electrical and atomic effect, while the formation of a sun, or fixed star, is a secondary, macrocosmic effect.

How shameful it is that many of today's so-called modern theologians continue to maintain that the creation of light *before* the sun conclusively demonstrates the mythological, physically senseless nature of Genesis. They contend that light can come only from a sun. I have long since ceased to expect others to share my personal admiration for the story of Genesis. But I am repeatedly frightened by the fanaticism of many young theology students, who reject outright all discussion of that story and of the miracles. They insist that their professors, using classical methods of biblical and textual criticism, have proven beyond a doubt that Genesis and the miracles are just myths, lacking any physically explicable meaning or even a basis for serious discussion. It is painful, as I have often experienced, to see an assembly of students with scientists, engineers, economists, and theologians, for what happens is what Otto Weber described—the theologians deny while the others confess their faith.

It would be imprudent to ask the young theology students and their teachers to throw their skillful methods of textual criticism overboard all at once because of advances in physics. I merely object to the arrogance of the belief that the concepts of the classics are appropriate for assessing the realities of physics. I hope no one will be offended if such an attitude arouses strong doubts in my mind about the validity and usefulness of these concepts derived from classical studies. Those who have not been endowed with better knowledge can serenely look upon the story of Genesis as a myth. They can still learn much from it and be fine Christians. But haughty judgment of God's revelations in the Bible and in nature leads to obduracy and to downfall in the Judgment, as Romans 1:22, I Corinthians 1:19,20, and Matthew 13:13,14 testify.

5. COMPLEMENTARITY[1,2,4]

Bohr's discovery some fifty years ago intensified curiosity about the nature of light. Two hundred years of experiments had indicated the wave nature of light. But many experiments since the discovery of the photoelectric effect have shown that light takes the form of energy quanta, i.e., that it has a particle nature. The wave nature fit the concept that a single photon took the form of a meter-long wave train. The particle nature best fit the concept that a photon is much smaller than one hundred-millionth of a centimeter when it is released or absorbed in an atom or by an electron.

I still recall vividly how a former Professor, using the blackboard, explained these difficulties to us students in the Twenties. If one pictured a photon as an "elementary wavelet," one could imagine it spreading through space from its point of origin. But in the instant of its absorption by an atom, it suddenly contracted into a minute dot. This was unimaginable. To make a gross analogy, we were expected to accept the following: the lightwave train is pictured as an express train with several hundred compartments (i.e., wavelengths). The express train enters a railroad station (i.e., an atom) on a vacant track (i.e., electron orbit). However, the entry takes place instantaneously, and the railroad station itself is no bigger than a model toy, of the type we give our children for Christmas.

This analogy is intended to show what is demanded of our power of intuition when, on the basis of numerous experiments, we sometimes attribute the traditional wave nature to light and, on the basis of numerous other experiments, we at other times attribute a particle nature to it. It is not just that our minds are unable to grasp this wave-corpuscle duality in concrete terms; it is also that to consider both characteristics *simultaneously* present in a single photon *in one and the same experiment* is absurd.

The situation was greatly aggravated by the discovery in the Twenties that the wave-particle duality applied not only to light but to particles previously considered decidedly material in nature, i.e., to electrons and atoms and molecules of all kinds and sizes. Streams of these material particles displayed a typical wave character in certain experiments. These waves, discovered by de Broglie, are called matter waves.[4] They are of major significance: if an electron microscope can enlarge an object a thousand times more than an ordinary light miscroscope, the reason is that the wavelengths of electrons' matter waves are much smaller than the wavelengths of visible light.

At the beginning of the twentieth century, physics was still thought to be concerned with either compact matter or light waves. But today, matter also partakes of a wave character and light of a material character. "Either-or" has given way to "not only-but also." The old physics was not set aside; it was merely further developed and improved. Though our power to grasp it fails, this "not only-but also" is physical reality. Niels Bohr coined the term "complementarity" for this physical state. The word comes from the Latin verb *complere* (to fill or complete). Every phenomenon, including energy, manifests itself complimentarily, depending on the experimental conditions, as either particles or waves, but never as both simultaneously. Figuratively speaking—and we shall return to this in the final chapter—every phenomenon manifests itself either as a person or as an oscillating state, depending on the environmental conditions. One senses here a similarity to theological concepts. But more on that later.

6. STATISTICS

a. *Example 1: Atomic Physics*[7]

As suggested at one point above, an atom consists of a heavy nucleus with a shell of electrons around it. Every chemical element is made of such atoms. Some elements have atomic nuclei that decay spontaneously over time. Such elements are described as radioactive. The best known, discovered by Pierre and Marie Curie, is radium, i.e., that which radiates. Radioactive decay can consist of the emission of alpha particles (identical to helium nuclei), beta particles (identical to electrons), or gamma particles (identical to shortwave X-rays). The end product of decay is a stable element, in the case of radium a kind of lead. Artificial radioactive elements are produced in atomic reactors, and their radiation is used to treat cancer and other diseases. The law of radioactive decay phenomena is well known. In its so-called half-life, a gram of a radio-active substance decays by precisely half, or 1/2 gram. Half of the remaining half then decays in the next half-life, and so on. A half-life may be 1,000 years, but it may range from millionths of a second to millions of years.

One gram of such material contains over one billion times one trillion individual atoms. If I ask when any particular atom will decay, I face an insoluble task. It could be in ten minutes, or a million years, or any other time. The probability of its decaying within 1,000 years, assuming a half-life of 1,000 years, is high. But probability is not certainty. If it has not decayed in 100 million years, a "miracle" has happened to it—a unique, all but impossible phenomenon outside the framework of normal events.

Many processes in nature involve tremendous numbers of individual actors, for all matter consists of atoms or of combinations of atoms known as molecules. Description of the state or behavior of a large number of individuals is called statistics. The individuals may be identical, or indistinguishable from each other, and may also be independent of each other. They may also be different from, and to some degree dependent upon, each other; in that case, the situation is far more difficult to grasp. Though a miracle is a rare, or perhaps even unique, event or experience, quite out of the ordinary, it can with comparative ease, as our example shows, be placed in a statistical framework. It has no intrinsic peculiarity requiring that it be placed outside that framework. Thus, a miracle, though a rarity to be sure, is a phenomenon of natural law, for statistics are of the essence of natural law.

One may object at this point that our ordinary schoolbooks give no indication that *all* natural laws may have statistical character. But it should not be forgotten that the fact that all energy is corpuscular, operating in the form of atoms or quanta, makes *every* physical process in the macrocosm a phenomenon involving massive numbers of particles subject to statistical laws. In deriving a formula from experimental results, one is usually forced to make the tacit assumption that the overwhelming majority of particles from the microcosm act alike. We cannot start from statistical suppositions, simply because our detailed knowledge is still so very inadequate. But that will change in time as we develop our ability to understand events in the macrocosm as nothing more than consequences of the statistical behavior of atoms and energy quanta in the microcosm.

b. Abuse of Statistics

Statistics are popularly considered rather disreputable. It is said that one can prove anything at all with statistics. For example, certain scientists have recently used them to make even biblical miracles plausible—and everyone knows they are "only myths."

This attitude calls for comment. Considering the way government agencies, parties, magazines, and anyone else with an ax to grind misuse statistics through surveys, their poor reputation is understandable. The worthlessness of such statistics is often immediately apparent from the leading nature of the questions asked or from the absence of significant questions, in which the pollster for personal reasons lacks interest. The simpler and more neutral the subject of a statistic is (e.g., income, rent, building construction, head of cattle, stands of trees, diseases), the more cleanly and precisely it can be stated. On the other hand, the more the subject of a statistic is related to the personality (e.g., looking at people from the religious or sexual standpoint), the less objective value the statistic has. The same is true if, due to the questioner's bias against religious precepts or his desire to assure certain results in advance, the factors whose influence is to be examined are one-sided or mutually dependent. Our popular magazines are filled with such negative examples. As so often in life, however, one should not be deterred by bad examples from making use of what is basically a good thing. The proof of the value of statistical methods is seen in the insurance industry.

c. *Example 2 and Spiritualist Spooks*

I shall now cite examples to show that the laws of statistics make miracles plausible. For this consideration it makes little difference whether we thereby identify the way they actually happened. As our research marches on, we often learn several ways of obtaining the same effect.

The sensation of our skin, called temperature, is provoked by the drumming of air molecules against the skin. The impact velocity varies from a few millimeters per second to several thousand meters per second. At room temperature the overwhelming majority of molecules travel at about 300 meters per second. Not only do their velocities vary, but they move back and forth in many different directions as well—in what we call a statistical distribution. They also strike the table top in my room from above and from below. One of the innumerable possibilities in the distribution of movements of the air molecules is for most of them above the table top to fly vertically upward and for most of them below to do the same. In that case, the table top will rise. If that molecular motion then repeats itself, the table will remain suspended and move slightly through the room. What appears to the layman a miraculous suspension of the law of gravity would to the physicist merely be the effect on a large body of an exceptional distribution of molecular kinetic energy. On a small scale, this phenomenon is quite familiar to him as the walking motion. It bears the humble name "Brownian molecular movement." Discovered under the microscope in 1827, it was not explained for another half century. In the microscopic kingdom, where far fewer molecules are involved, this otherwise very improbable event is more common. One can watch a very small object, propelled by molecular collisions, hover and skip in the field of vision. The macroscopic case of the table, on the other hand, is calculated to be so improbable as never to happen, unless we one day discover a mechanism for controlling the motion of a large number of molecules and causing a table to hover in the air. The New Testament miracles in which Jesus walks on water, Peter attempts with some success to do the same, and a body rises upward to heaven may conceivably fit into this category of phenomena.

It is often said that spiritualists have the power to bring about the phenomenon of table motion which physicists discuss. It never fails that those who seek to persuade me of this are, of all people, people who consider themselves religious and devout. If I then demand to see the phenomenon in order to subject it to scientific test, they throw up their hands imploringly, insisting that such an action would damage my religious life and prayer. It never occurs to them that God watches over a religious physicist who possesses specialized knowledge which they lack. Scientists have investigated certain unexplained cases of psychokinesis, i.e., of movement under the impact or in the presence of a mind, but these cases have nothing to do with spiritualistic table movements. These Christian brethren absolutely refuse to admit the possibility that self deception and tricks, rather than spirits and miraculous powers, may be involved in spiritualism. My impression is that they believe deeply in the reality of spiritual apparitions, even if they take no personal part in them.

Every scientist has a human ideal after whom he patterns his thought and action. I, as an experimental physicist, have Michael Faraday as my scientific and spiritual ideal. I try to think the way he thought. Faraday (1791-1867), the most successful experimenter of all time and the discoverer of the law of induction, which receives its technological expression in generators, was at the same time a deeply devout Christian. At one point he was interested enough to accept the invitations of spiritualists. He later constructed and publicly displayed an apparatus that enabled everyone to see for himself how tables were made to move. As he wrote in a letter,* "I have been disappointed so many times by manifestations of spirits that I don't have the heart to pay any more attention to them. . . . If the spirits have anything to communicate that isn't to-

---

* From the German version by Hermann Helmholtz.—Trans.

tally useless, I'll leave it to them to find ways and means to get my attention. I am sick of them." On another occasion he wrote the following about the type of event we described above: "As soon as the spirits repeal the law of gravity or cause motion, . . . as soon as they do these or other things better than a juggler can, . . . they'll have my attention. But until such things happen, I have no time either for spirits and their followers or for correspondence on the subject."

d.   Three Cases from the Bible

In daily life we almost never experience any spectacular events which, as in the aforementioned cases of atoms or molecules, result from the spontaneous coordination of immense numbers of agents or factors of the same kind. The factors involved are usually very diverse and often bear no clear relationship to each other. Each factor in turn may be composed of many microcosmic elements. The precise details cannot be established by measurement and need not interest us here. The various factors, each of which may function at one of many different levels of intensity, may interact in such a way that the result is an event so extraordinary and rare as to be considered a miracle. Let us assume that five factors, each of which can occur at three different levels of intensity, are interacting. How many possible combinations are there? The answer is "15 factorial." That means $1 \times 2 \times 3 \times 4 \times 5 \times 6 \times \ldots 12 \times 13 \times 14 \times 15 = 1,307,674,368,000$ possibilities, i.e., over 1.3 trillion! Even if the overwhelming majority of these combinations produce effects that are scarcely distinguishable from each other, exceptional combinations, characterized by a special order of the components and producing effects that seem to be miracles, are also among them.

Let us examine three concrete examples from the Bible. The first is the burning bush seen by Moses.[13] It was a Dictamnus albus, also known as diptam. For the bush to be in flames without being consumed, at least five factors had to be interacting—solar irradiation, windlessness, blooming stage, external temperature, and absence of buzzing insects. Each of the five factors has several subsidiary conditions, e.g., for solar irradiation—season, time of day, length of irradiation; for blooming stage—number of blossoms, output of volatile aroma, flash point. Only in the rare case when long-lasting, intense solar irradiation heats the volatile aroma of a large bush beyond its flash point, and when there is no disturbance caused by wind or winged insects, only then will the ether from the flowers burn with a reddish flame. While this rare phenomenon can of course be produced more easily in laboratories, it rarely occurs spontaneously in nature. It has occurred in Central Europe, however, as for example in the district of Kielce south of Warsaw in 1965.

The crossing of the Red Sea by the Israelites is another example.[13] The following factors played a role: wind direction, windspread, specific tide conditions, the sea floor and sea depth, and a fiery pillar of clouds. In this case an unusual meteorological phenomenon was involved. Except for the last-named factor, which is difficult to explain, all of these factors, each of which is in turn of complex composition, is always at work in the Red Sea just as everywhere else. But this time all the factors supported each other so strongly that the sea-floor land bridge was kept open for an entire night, permitting the passage of the Israelites. This event was an affirmative miracle for the Israelites, and a negative one, i.e., a catastrophe, for the Egyptians. Meteorology teaches us that many factors must combine to bring about a rare catastrophe, the type about which we read in the newspapers. One objective of meteorological research is to be able to warn us in time, on the basis of constant observation and the statistics of countless good and bad events, when a dangerous extreme case is developing. Unfortunately, success is often quite incomplete, for the very reason that an extraordinary case is not of the normal, easily studied kind and, because of its rarity, is difficult to comprehend fully.

My third example is the phenomenon of the star of the Wise Men.[13] Astrophysics helps us to understand the distribution, development, composition, and stability of the stars. Among the possible inner states of a star is that of its imminent explosion. When the explosion occurs, the star flares up brightly. According to the statistics on stars, such an event should occur within view of the earth every 400 years or so, very roughly speaking. We of course cannot say just when it will happen, or just where in the sky. But that is not so important. This is, then, a rare event, but not so rare as to be called an astronomical miracle.

Some contend that the star of the Wise Men was one of those now precisely predictable conjunctions of the planets Jupiter, Saturn, and Mars, known as a great conjunction, rather than a single star. In my opinion, however, that is not what the biblical text says. Specific evidence was supplied by Ignatius, the second Bishop of Antioch, when he wrote in his second epistle to the Ephesians, around the year 110, of the "inexpressibly strong light" of a single star, known to scientists as a supernova. But the constellation of planets is also significant. When such a constellation occurred in 1604, a new twinkling star *also* appeared in the sky at the same time. There is not the slightest physical relationship between the constellation of planets and the new star; but the coincidence of the two events was a fact. It even caused the great astronomer Kepler to calculate whether such a constellation had occurred around the time of the beginning of the Christian era as well. His finding was affirmative, which indicates that Jesus was born at least six years *before* the so-called Christian era began. The two similar cases were separated by 1600 years. When will the coincidence reoccur? The great conjunctions, which are precisely predictable, occur every 800 years or so. Supernovae, on the other hand, are not seen at precisely 400-year intervals; the intervals may differ considerably, ranging, for example, from 300 to 500 years. Hence, the occurrence of both events within the same year, which is what we are after, can perhaps be expected only at intervals of tens of thousands of years. The main reason then for classifying the star of the

Wise Men as a miracle is that it caused the Magi to undertake an expedition and that it proclaimed the birth of Jesus.

In addition to the above cases, let us look at one from daily life. Two men of the same age, each wishing to take out a twenty-year life insurance policy, submitted completed medical reports to the insurance official. One was then required to pay higher monthly premiums than the other. The former was recorded as having many physical problems; according to the mortality statistics, he had only a few years left to live. The other man was found to be "the picture of health"; the statistics indicated that he would live for a long time. Both men asked the official to tell them, with as much precision as he had used in computing the premiums, how long they were expected to live. The official was at a total loss to answer. His statistics told him what percentage of his hundred thousand clients would die at a given age, but he could not apply the statistics to any single individual. His situation was the same as that of the observer in the above-described example of the radioactive decay. As it happened, the man who appeared to be "the picture of health" died unexpectedly a few years later, while the sickly man lived to be over ninety. The latter case could be taken almost as a miracle. This seemingly total failure of the statistics stemmed from the fact that they were designed to take into account only bodily diseases and states of health. They did not take account, for example, of the sickly man's fighting spirit and good habits of living or of the healthy man's poor style of living and lack of courage in facing life. In other words, the statistics ignored some fundamental factors.

I have used a few examples, the number of which could be multiplied at will, to show the statistical outlook of physics. They should suffice to show that one cannot simply dismiss the biblical accounts as myths. But since even the most complicated event in the macrocosm is based on microcosmic processes, there remains a theoretically undeterminable uncertainty factor in at least one group of contributing atoms, as we shall see in sections 7 and 8. It is this factor that decides whether the event shall actually take place or shall be dismantled behind the scenes and prevented from happening. This factor is not within our reach.

e. Distribution Curves

What has been said above can be further illustrated by a graphic presentation. This is the usual way of giving an overview of a statistical process. The thick curve, called a distribution curve, lies between two straight lines with measurements marked off. The vertical line, also known

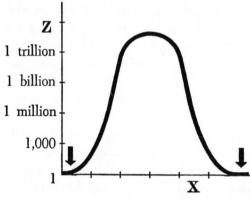

as the ordinate, shows a series of numbers Z. Starting with 1, I have each quantity in the series 1,000 times larger than its predecessor, so that I reach the large numbers quickly and the total picture can be seen at a glance. These quantities symbolize large numbers of different things, such as atoms, impacts, people, or influencing factors. The horizontal line, also called the abscissa, is for the things on which the statistics are being compiled. Thus, the abscissa represents not just numbers but qualities, such as amounts of energy, degrees of temperature, target fields, attained ages, heights, or depths. The distribution curve represents the physical relationship between qualities X and numbers Z.

The right and left ends of such distribution curves are the rare, bizarre events that we perceive as miracles. Let us take the burning bush as an example.[13] The usual temperatures around the bush lie in the middle part of the X-axis, under the hump of the curve. They result from the influence of billions of combinations of the factors listed in the preceding section. It is of course possible over the course of many years that one summer day will bring winter temperatures to the place where the bush is located. This would be shown at a point on the far left of the distribution curve, near the thick arrow. But nothing special occurs. Another day, however, will be very hot, and will combine the additional conditions discussed earlier. On that rare day, shown on the far right of the curve near the other thick arrow, if the temperature in the bush reaches the flash point of the volatile oil, the bush will catch fire. I do not know just how high the temperature would have to be; I would estimate it at between fifty and seventy degrees, depending on the composition of the ether.

Let us examine the crossing of the Red Sea by the people of Israel as another example. The abscissa on our graph now represents the depth of the sea. Under normal climatic conditions, i.e., on hundreds of thousands or millions of days, the water depth is usually from one to two meters. On very rare occasions, shown at the arrow on the far right, the depth reaches five to ten meters above normal. For that to happen, a storm and a spring tide must occur simultaneously. This, too, is a kind of miracle, physically speaking, though it is not so perceived. Such events have occurred quite recently, as in the storm tide on the lower Elbe River in 1962 and on the coast of Bangladesh a decade later. The miracle that saved the Israelites would be located near the left arrow on the distribution curve. Climatic factors lowered the water level one night to such an extent as to expose the land bridge under the surface, making a crossing possible at shallow points. Sand-filling and silting since that event have caused the sea to recede, separating the Red Sea proper from the inland lake that lies to the north of it. I shall content myself with these two examples, leaving it to the reader to analyze numerous other biblical accounts from a statistical viewpoint.

So far, we have described in statistical terms the interaction of large numbers of particles or of individually known factors. Statistics have enabled us to appreciate the extreme cases which are perceived as miracles. But there are miracles, in the present day as well as in the Bible, which we apparently cannot fit into a statistical framework. Such is the case of a cripple who suddenly tosses his crutches away and walks normally. But one should bear in mind that the greater our knowledge of all the factors involved, the more assuredly we can accommodate extreme cases in our statistics on healing. This becomes more difficult, however, as the object involved becomes more complex in its makeup; and man, with his physical, mental, and somatic factors, is a highly complex being. We must also remember that the statistical method in physics was discovered and incorporated into distribution curves by Maxwell, Clausius, and Boltzmann only 100 years ago, after preparatory mathematical work by Gauss. When a true scientist learns of unusual biological miracles, he does not give up or attribute them to the supernatural. He waits patiently until new discoveries and knowledge make it possible to explore the nature of these miracles too.

f. Where Statistics Fail

Statistics take account of many factors and embrace rare, extreme cases which people call miracles. But one does not exhaust the content of biblical miracles merely by recognizing the consistency of extreme cases with natural law. Our comments up to now have been somewhat one-sided; they must be significantly expanded. The really miraculous part of the miracles is the time—not the form—in which they manifest themselves. A person who denies the reality of a miracle by the same token blinds himself to the insight that God spoke and acted through that miracle at a specific point in time. No man could have decided just what that time should be; he could at most have helped to decide through prayer. Thus, the critics do not take the point in time seriously either; rather, they classify it as one of the mythical elements. The biblical account retains only existential value; it is seen as portraying in naive, picturesque language a situation that reoccurs and must be mastered a thousand times in our own day. The biblical account thus has no higher worth than a modern account of a similar situation in daily life. Pulpit or radio sermons delivered from this perspective may be well and pleasantly written, but they have little connnection with the true and genuine Jesus and YHWH of the Bible.

The more frequently an event that is included in statistics can happen, the easier it is to determine a precise time of occurrence for it. Such events fall under the hump of our distributive curve, which is the location of most events Z. On the other hand, the rarer an event, the harder it is to determine a precise time for its occurrence. One can only assign a probability to it. If the relationship of the event to the total number of possible events is defined in probabilistic terms, the occurrence of a miracle within the foreseeable future, lying at one end of our distribution curve, becomes highly unlikely. But even the greatest improbability cannot rule out the possibility that the event will occur tomorrow.

I repeat: the really miraculous element in the biblical miracles is the time of their occurrence; for, insofar as we possess the necessary scientific knowledge, we know that the occurrence of the event itself is a definite possibility, as long as we wait long enough. According to the *biblical* accounts, the time at which a miracle occurs is determined by things that cannot be conceived or influenced physically, i.e., the spiritual distress of a person or a community, the answering of a prayer ("Out of the depths I cry to thee, O Lord! Lord, hear my voice!"), and, lastly and chiefly, God's sovereign intervention.

These accounts elicit renewed criticism. Let us agree, say the critics, that the miracles are phenomenologically plausible and therefore physically possible. Yet if a miracle, understood as a statistically rare event, is produced by forces that are not specifically physical (God, spirit, or prayer), are we not dealing, at least insofar as the time is concerned, with the supernaturalism that has been so far sharply rejected? And isn't supernaturalism rejected by existentialist, demythologizing theology?

This criticism rests ultimately on a mechanical-materialistic view of the world, as described in chapter 5. The modernistic theologians who subscribe to this view assume that every event can be understood and even predicted if one possesses sufficient knowledge of all the influencing factors. In other words, it should be possible to achieve any desired degree of understanding of the causes of any event, even one regarded as a miracle, and, if necessary, to predict or produce it. These modernistic theologians insist that the law of causality is applicable in its usual, strict sense. As one of them, H. W. Bartsch, wrote in his book *Christ without Myth* (Stuttgart, 1953), "Only if one recognizes this law can one talk to modern man. Any other talk seems unreasonable to him. He feels that, like baby talk, it is below him." But this is the very sort of attitude that quantum physics challenges. Quantum physics has crucially enlarged the use of statistics in physics. It substitutes knowledge derived from experimentation for the supernaturalism, based in materialism, of modernistic theologians. We shall return to this subject later.

7. INDETERMINACY [4,6,7]

We now turn again to the problem of atomic physics—radioactive decay—with which we dealt in the first section on statistics. We said there that the atoms of some chemical elements decay spontaneously due to radiation from their nuclei. The law of decay, discovered half a century ago, is the same for all elements, though each has a different half-life. No laws have been found to explain the moment at which a given atom happens to decay. Yet knowledge of such laws would be of great interest, for it is not the vast multitude of atoms that brings about the decay of any single one of them; rather, the contrary is the case: the countless atoms that sooner or later decay supply the basis for the statistics on which a mathematical law of decay is based. Nothing would be more appealing than to probe the interior of the atom, i.e., its nucleus and shell, with the help of appropriate instruments, to find the reasons for the time and cause of decay. But the desire to examine the interior of the atom meets with an insoluble dilemma. Though we intend to engage only in physics at this point, we find ourselves confronting a theological problem.

Two types of probes are available to us. On the one hand, there are the particles—electrons, protons, neutrons, etc.—of which atoms are built; on the other, there are photons of different energy levels. We shall consider only the latter. In accordance with an old law of physics, the shorter the wavelength of the light used to illuminate and study the form and structure of an object, the greater the precision with which the job can be done. This can be made clear to the layman by a simple illustration. If he holds his hand in front of a transmitter of ordinary electric waves, such as one used in diathermy, the inside of his hand will remain invisible. But if he places his hand under a strong incandescent bulb he will detect the faint outlines of his bones in the reddish light that shines through. And if X-rays penetrate his hand, the bone structure will become visible in detail. From electrical waves to visible light to X-rays, the wavelengths have diminished many billions of times.

To study the interior of an atom, which has a total diameter of about one-ten millionth of a centimeter, one must use the extremely short-wave X-rays known as gamma-rays. Now, the extremely short wavelength l is accompanied by the very high frequency v, since wavelength and frequency are related to the speed of light c by the formula $l \cdot v = c$. This is where the "but" comes in. Gamma radiation is not just light with a wave character, for pursuant to Planck's law it partakes of a corpuscular character as well. Despite the minute value of h, the photons in gamma radiation, because of their colossal frequency v, have such high energy $E = h \cdot v$ that they change and sometimes shatter the interior of the atoms they penetrate.

Hence our insoluble dilemma: in shortening the wavelength of light so that we can look into the interior of the atom with greater clarity and precision, we simultaneously increase the energy of the light (now interpreted as corpuscular) so greatly that it disturbs and destroys the interior of the atom. This dilemma is an expression of the complementarity discussed in section 5 above. It cannot be avoided by using material particles, such as the neutrons discovered by Chadwick, which are able to penetrate deeply because they lack any charge; the reason is that they, too, partake of complementarity, possessing a wave as well as a corpuscular character. All this applies to the atomic shell, made up of electrons, as well as to the nucleus. When an electron collides with light, changes inevitably occur in both of them.

We must recognize that our chances of observing and measuring the inside of an atom the way we have long been accustomed to doing in the macrocosm, with its tremendous conglomerations of atoms, are slim. In the 1920's, Werner Heisenberg gave mathematical expression to this uncertainty, implying that man has reached a fundamental limit to his cognition and ability to measure physically. By "fundamental" it is meant that no solution will ever be possible. Other never-laws of this type exist. Thus, the first principle of thermodynamics rules out the possibility that a perpetual motion machine—a machine that creates something out of nothing—could ever exist. The principle that it is impossible to square the circle with a pair of compasses and a ruler is also known; indeed, the "squaring of the circle" has become a proverbial synonym for impossibility and absurdity.

An argument as weighty as Heisenberg's had to be challenged, tested, and if necessary refined. But it could not be shaken, for the weight of experimental evidence supports it. It does not represent grandiose wishful thinking or a manifestation of resignation. Heisenberg's perception is grounded in the knowledge of physicists that Planck's constant h is an absolute universal constant of nature, not a divisible quantity.

This perception contains a theological affirmation. However, I do not reproach the modernistic theologians for the difficulty they have in incorporating such scientific perceptions and the consequences of these perceptions deeply into their thinking. But I do seriously reproach them for failing for decades even to take note of these things. With their myth of demythologizing they consciously try to foist a one-sided, false interpretation of the miracles upon their students—our future pastors.

There are various names for the Heisenberg principle in its mathematical form—indeterminacy relation, uncertainty relation, inaccuracy relation. The choice depends somewhat on the application intended. As we know, every measurement we make in physics suffers from some degree of error. The imperfect accuracy of our measuring devices prevents us from determining the quantity precisely enough or from perceiving it firmly enough. The indeterminacy relation combines the errors in measurement of two variables, the product of which represents an effect. Yet the effect is strictly controlled by the value h of Planck's constant. The effect may be larger than or equal to, but *never* smaller than, the value of the constant! In other words, in the atomic domain, as we approach our limit, effects become equal to the value of Planck's constant, and a certain imprecision, *not* resulting from the shortcomings of even our most precise measuring instruments, inevitably exists. Two such measured variables are the momentum (which incorporates the velocity) and the position of a particle. Another pair of measured variables is the kinetic energy B of a particle and the time in which we observe it and in which we seek to make measurements on it. The imprecision of B is written $\triangle$ B, while that of t is written $\triangle$ t. They are combined in the formula $\triangle$ B $\cdot$ $\triangle$ t $\geqq$ h.

We shall adduce two examples to illustrate this situation. An atom consists of a nucleus and a shell of electrons. As we indicated in section 4, an electron surrenders a photon when it moves from a higher to a lower energy level. The required energy can be determined with precision. If we now expend it, we still cannot say when the electron jumps, giving off a flash of light. But if we use enormous numbers of atoms and a larger beam of light for our experiment, enough of them will immediately give the desired experimental result.

A second example: Take a disc with a fine hole in it. Let an atom, an electron, or a photon travel to the hole at a precisely known velocity and pass through the hole to an intercepting screen behind the disc. Where will it strike? The layman will naturally assume that the point of impact is the point on the screen directly opposite the hole. Actually, however, the point of impact cannot be determined. But if the experiment is done with a great quantity of particles, i.e., with a beam of particles, one discerns the concentric rings created by their impact.

The statements in the above examples do not mean that we are unable to determine with precision each individual value or quality of an atom that may be of interest to us—position, velocity, energy value, time factors, etc. What we are inherently incapable of doing, and yet would like to do, however, is to observe and measure *all* the parameters, such as place, time, and energy, of a *single* atom simultaneously and with the greatest possible accuracy. An individual atom or elementary particle never reveals more than one of its qualities at a time; it denies us the simultaneous knowledge of any others. Atoms and elementary particles do not exist as simple physical objects. They are not steel bullets or tennis balls in miniature.

8. DETERMINATION AND CAUSALITY[1,2,4,6,7,10]

Unfortunately, few people understand just how fundamental the findings described in the preceding section are, or just how far beyond physics their significance extends. We are proud to have discovered the atomic structure of matter and light and thus to have found the key to unlocking vast amounts of energy for nuclear power plants and expeditions to distant planets. We are as proud as those who built the Tower of Babel. We are even proud of God's statement in the eleventh chapter of Genesis: "Nothing that they propose to do will now be impossible for them." At that time people built an enormous tower; today they accumulate atom bombs. The words God spoke then are just as valid today, for the power of malice and selfishness in the hearts of men is no different today from then, and people think that God is far away. Every atom in the entire world presents a limit that can be neither overcome nor penetrated by physics. This should lead one to suspect that God, apparently so distant and perhaps even non-existent, may actually be amazingly close.

Let us look again, from the standpoint of the concept of causality, at the physical knowledge presented in the preceding section. In the case of large objects, such as airplanes, electrical radar waves can be used to determine with precision their positions (distance and altitude), changes of course, and all other behavioral parameters. Strictly objective surveillance of an airplane can be maintained by various control towers. The airplane itself has no impact on the surveillance of its overall situation. As we have seen, it is impossible to determine objectively the overall situation of an object in the microcosm, such as an atom or an elementary atomic particle, even if we were to look at it from several different points of view. In other words, atoms and their components cannot be observed objectively in space. The more objective an observer of the atom tries to be, i.e., the more determined he is to obtain only information that has its source and existence within the atom itself, the greater his subjective influence becomes. The information he obtains is far more determined by measuring instruments he uses than by the atom itself. The *only* devices that can be used in diagnosing an atom cause significant changes in it.

The point can be further illustrated by an example out of daily life: A doctor examines a patient. He makes his diagnosis by percussion, use of a stethoscope and thermometer, needle biopsy, and X-ray. But he might also proceed in a different manner, resorting to the knife to reveal what he wishes to see. In the former case, he makes a judgment without changing the patient. In the latter, the knife changes the patient, and may even damage him so severely as to justify the conclusion, "Operation successful, patient dead." With atoms, however, we have no alternative to the second approach, for the smallest usable knife has a standard size; i.e., the action quantum has a fixed value and cannot be served up in a smaller dose.

In encroaching upon an atomic system in this—necessarily never objective—manner, *we* freely determine our conduct. What is the result? Like human beings, the atomic system behaves freely. In accordance with the indeterminacy relation, it has the freedom to decide when and how to react to our stimulus. Its freedom is of course not absolute, being held within the confines of the indeterminacy law. But the time margin, represented by Δ t, is there. This freedom of decision, in the guise of a time margin, counterbalances what is called the determinacy or determination of an event. Determinacy denotes strict predetermination and inevitability. According to the old concept obtained in the macrocosm, if a cause is unequivocally known the consequences are unequivocally determined. Thus, a precisely conceived experiment, however often repeated, could have only one result. In the microcosm, on the other hand, each time an experiment is repeated the result is different. The atomic particles fired through the hole, in the example cited in the preceding section, strike the screen behind the hole at different, but unpredictable, points. We can express only a probability as to where the particle will strike. The point on the screen directly behind the hole is the most probable. Other less probable points lie in rings around that midpoint. To involve all the points in these concentric circles in a single experiment, one fires a stream of billions of particles through the hole. With these enormous numbers of particles, the result is certain; one can draw the rings in advance. But that cannot be done with a single particle, for in the framework of the indeterminacy relation, a single particle retains its freedom of decision.

The ancient principle that, if all disturbances and distortions are eliminated, a cause leads to a precisely predictable result remained uncontested until this century. Cause and effect were thought to be equivalent. *Causa adaequat effectum.* This relationship is called the *law of causation.* There had long been uncertainty regarding its applicability in biology and psychology, particularly with respect to free will in man. But materialism, i.e., the delusion that denies God and spirit, overcame this uncertainty when de Lamettries' shrewdly written book *The Human Machine* appeared around 1750. The behavior of a machine, including a computer, is determined in a strictly causal way. It follows human instructions precisely. Viewing man in the final analysis as a being mechanically controlled by a law of evolution, materialism describes man in the same way.[7]

Now that atoms are known to be physical realities, we must understand that laws other than those ruling the macrocosm apply to the microcosm. The old law of causation is replaced by a *causality principle.* It states that a strict law of causation does not hold in the microcosm, among atoms, their component parts, or photons. Only with the tremendous agglomerations of atomic systems characteristic of the macrocosm does the old law of causation reemerge; but even then, as we shall see, it can be interpreted only as a law of probability. The causality principle is another illustration of the point we emphasized in chapter 3 and again in the second section of chapter 7—that modern physics is a further development, not a negation, of the older physics.

Many people, and particularly the philosophers and existentialist theologians who see the foundations of their theories being washed away, do not like these aspects of the causality principle. The main objection they raise is that these concepts of physics contradict the principles of logic, and that anything illogical must be wrong. Such arguments have been advanced since ancient times. Logic once insisted that the sun revolves around the earth, and not vice versa. Later, logic was called upon to do battle with the relativity theory, since the speed of light logically cannot be a constant in all systems moving in relation to each other. Physics, however, is not subservient to logical thought as colored by tradition. Rather, the logic of physics requires that thought be governed by the realities and truths of nature. Even that which, by habit or conviction, we call logic requires constant verification.

The new causality principle, manifested most clearly in the uncertainty relation, endows the statistical picture of physics, treated in the sixth section of chapter 7, with significance far surpassing the bounds of physics and is helpful to theology. As we indicated, it is possible through statistics to interpret rare events, deemed miraculous, as being fully consistent with natural law. Arguing in terms of the older physics, which was useful to materialism, one may still maintain that a strict law of causation underlies a given miracle, and that only our inadequate state of scientific knowledge prevents us from understanding the causal background of the miracle. At one time we were able to understand natural law only in terms of causal determinacy. But modern physics has fundamentally changed all that. Whether a statistic deals with identical individuals or with a heterogeneous group of things, a conglomeration of atomic systems in which indeterminate processes are taking place is always involved. Something may happen in one or more atoms that affects the entire conglomeration, converting what would have been a statistically usual case into a unique extreme, or producing an unstable situation that, unbeknown to anyone, eliminates itself just before causing such an extreme. One can imagine a considerable number of cases in which the action of rays upon an atom causes the latter to store energy which, after an absolutely indeterminate time period, sets in motion a radiation process which, like an avalanche or chain reaction, spreads from that atom and produces a positive miracle or a negative miracle, such as an explosion or other catastrophe.

There are materialists who are honestly convinced that all events occur in a strictly causal manner and that, by taking appropriate steps, they can provide every conceivable guarantee for their own lives and the lives of their loved ones. To such people the physicist's assertion that there can on principle be no such guarantee, determinacy, assurance, or whatever else one might call it, is a source of considerable insecurity. Physics cannot rule out, and must in fact accept, the possibility that a good force (God) or an evil force (the Devil) intervenes to provoke an atomic reaction without in any sense doing violence to natural law. In so doing, physics does not overstep its competence; it merely states the limits of its competence. How many times in war has a man been untouched by shell fragments thanks to atomic processes that cause the shell to burst in such a way that he is not hit? In the same way, a long stored atomic process often influences the splintering at the decisive moment in such a way that he is hit. There is deep meaning in the fact that men pray to God in moments of need such as this. God really can help, for he is a close and powerful God.

To someone who looks at these things only from the standpoint of theology—or, to state it more simply, only from the standpoint of faith and prayer—it matters little *how* and in what way God helps. He is satisfied with the fact *that* God does so. But to someone who prefers to have these events and possibilities examined from the scientific standpoint as well, two questions arise.

The first question stems from the following line of reasoning: That which is common to all matter and all radiation is the energy, in the form of quanta, acting within them. Energy acts through time, but in the case of atomic processes determination of the precise time is surrounded by a greater or lesser degree of uncertainty. In our discussion of radioactive decay we have seen how enormous this uncertainty can be. Considering this uncertainty, even the physicist must officially concede the possibility of intervention by God. To use a vivid image, he admits that God can turn the levers and knobs of time. But the physicist must also concede this possibility not only to God's Holy Spirit but also to the Devil and to the human spirit, though in a different way in the case of the latter. Physics, however, can say nothing at all about *how* such intervention is effected. It is, after all, a fundamental article of the scientific view and of quantum physics that we can say nothing about the how and do no research on the how; it is senseless to construct models or pictures of it.

It must be emphasized, however, that physics gives fully as much justification to those who refuse to believe in God or to speak of him, and who see God as nothing more than a filler for the gaps in our knowledge, as to those who use the concept of God because of the idea of omnipotence associated with it.

The second question that always arises is the following: Let us assume that physics has led us to a knowledge barrier and has substituted a new causality principle, with its indeterminacies and probabilities, for the old law of causation, with its determinacies. Let us assume further that, on the grounds of this evidence alone, the arguments of modernistic theologians on the subject of miracles have become worthless. Could it not still be possible that new experiments will show us a way to break through the barrier? Did not Einstein himself often advance interesting, important arguments on this problem?

To begin with, the cold facts are that Einstein's objections were insufficient to provoke a reinterpretation of experimental reality, and that the growing volume of experimental evidence has failed to indicate a way out. As stated in chapter 3, on physics, the knowledge discovered in the present century will remain valid within the framework in which it was obtained. All that will happen is that the limits of its validity will be enlarged or somewhat contracted. It is quite possible that the concept of complementarity will have to be broadened, but it will not disappear. The indeterminacy relation may have to be refined, but the principle behind it will remain. It may be found that the new principle of causality has validity far beyond that which we now suspect in the microcosmic world. We shall gain new insights into further miracles, but we shall not discard those which we already have. Here I must emphasize once again the conclusion of physicists that physics will never be able to provide a mechanism for deciphering the ways in which God, the Spirit, and prayer operate. To us, this inability is a law of nature, not a question of scientific progress.

9. LIMITS OF KNOWLEDGE

If there is a barrier in every atom frustrating our cognitive abilities and our wish to unlock more of nature's secrets, that barrier exists throughout the world. I have spoken elsewhere[13] of the curtain that is drawn through the realm of nature. Figuratively speaking, that which is on this side of the curtain is the subject of physics; what is on the other side does not belong to the type of physics of which we are capable. In physics as we know it, we can make pictures and models of what lies behind the curtain, but they have no scientific value. Even in front of the curtain we are forced to portray the microcosm with pictures and models of the macrocosm if we are to achieve even a minimum of understanding. Thus, there is good reason that many physicists prefer to replace the concept of explaining nature in this area with the more modest concept of describing nature.[6] In any event, the Bible offers no explanations of nature. All the reporters limit themselves to descriptions of nature within the context of what God says and does, for the Bible is a religious, not a physics, text.

A physicist cannot prove—nor can he disprove—that God is behind the curtain or, still less, that this God is the Christian God, the Father of Jesus Christ. The work done in physics cannot deal with anything that demands more than a willingness to accept experimental and mathematical evidence. Hence, the recent discoveries of physics cannot lead one to Christian beliefs. But a physicist concerned with quantum physics is by nature a sinner, like all men; he, too, has heard about God and theology. He must not lightly ignore, therefore, what theology has to say.

The character of theology—i.e., of the theology we discussed in chapter 2 and subsequently—is that of revelation. This theology proclaims that God is *almighty,* and that, through his son Jesus Christ, he created the universe. Thus, there is no curtain with respect to God. God is on both sides of it. His Holy Spirit functions on both sides of the curtain. His laws of nature, being universal, are "very good." He alone can reveal that which, to our minds, lies on the other side. As indicated in the opening sentences of the epistle to the Hebrews, God has *in these last days* spoken *definitively* of these matters through Jesus. But the same theology teaches us also how the curtain and the separation of man from God were arrived at. The portrayal of the fall of man and the entire biblical subject of sin are beyond the scope of this book. Only one sentence is relevant to us at this point. Genesis 3:24 reads, in lapidary brevity: "So he drove out the man; and he placed at the east of the garden of Eden Cherubims, and a flaming sword which turned every way, to keep the way of the tree of life" (A.V.).

Luther's translation, "a naked, hewing sword," seems to overlook a matter of importance. The Zurich translation, "the flame of a waving sword," does not deal with it clearly enough. But three others—the German concordance translation, the King James or A.V., and the Septuagint (used by early Christians)—make it quite clear: the curtain is described as a "flaming sword which turned every way." Luther's interpretation is decidedly anthropomorphic. For this reason countless artists, like Schnorr von Carolsfeld, have exploited it, portraying Adam and Eve being driven from paradise by an angel with a sword in his hand. But the Bible is soberly written; at this point as at so many others, it presents things differently. God himself drove the couple out; he did not act through cherubim. The cherubim and the sword are separate from each other in the text. The sword has a positive character; it has something positive to say about nature.

I think that we in physics have an inkling of what "the flaming sword which turned every way" might really mean.

Just as the sword serves to separate in the military realm, so here it is the symbol of the division between this world and the world beyond, between Eden and earth. It has the quality of being "flaming," which could also be translated as "burning." It has the further quality of "turning every way," which could also be interpreted to mean "darting this way and that." Where there are flames, no man can pass without being consumed. We sometimes refer to impenetrable "walls of fire." Similarly, in physics one can attach concrete meaning to the concept of "turning every way." All matter consists of atoms. Every atom consists of a minute nucleus and a relatively enormous shell of electrons which revolve around the nucleus. Similar rotating and oscillating motions occur within the nuclei themselves. Much radiation consists of light of the most diverse wavelengths and has the nature of electromagnetic oscillation; that is, a magnetic field winds or revolves around each alternating electric field, an electric field winds or revolves around the magnetic field, and so on. But matter and radiation are just two different guises in which energy manifests itself. Thus, all energy is connected with rotating movement. In physics, systematic, rhythmical rotation is called oscillation. The world is an immense oscillating field. All action in this powerful oscillating field takes place in accordance with Planck's equation. Its characteristic is the constant h, which in the last analysis defines the limit of our cognitive abilities and possibilities. We might thus suspect that a physical reality that shapes our human world, rather than an unrealisic myth, lies behind the biblical image of a "flaming sword which turned every way."

I wish to stress explicitly that something of which we can have only the vaguest presentiment lies behind the biblical image. In no way does the image symbolize a devalued or diminished nature or a "fallen" creation.[13] This can be understood through physics. If it is the value of Planck's constant that ultimately limits *our* possibilities, we can still try to calculate mathematically what would happen if the constant were subdivided. We then find that subdividing the constant would wreak havoc with the entire scheme of the universe and its natural laws. However, this natural-law scheme of things, according to the Bible, existed *before* the fall of man and was "very good." Even the Apocalypse does not claim that the original, very good natural-law state of creation will be altered. The main characteristic of the new heaven and the new earth, that is, those from which the curtain will have disappeared, will be the fact that *righteousness* will dwell in them (II Peter 3:13). According to the fourteenth verse, it is this justice, and not new natural laws, that we must await. Other apostles speak in a similar vein (e.g., Paul in II Corinthians 5:17-21; and John in Revelation 21). Where Christ's blood and righteousness have become the honored dress of men, no longer is misuse, violence, or destruction visited upon nature.

We have spoken of the "flaming sword which turned every way." But what is the place of the cherubim? The text does not tell us. And it is highly doubtful that the examination of other passages that speak of cherubim would be of assistance (Ezekiel 10). It is certain, however, that the cherubim have tasks of dividing and guarding. In my view, this passage in the Bible employs the complementary mode of speech, presenting things to us now in the form of a person, now in the form of a state or condition.

10. QUANTUM BIOLOGY[5,7,14]

We have seen that events within a single atom are not strictly predictable. Forecasts of elementary processes can be made only in terms of probabilities. Determinacy and controllability attain their old reliability only in the case of matter in the macroscopic sense, where tremendous numbers of atoms are involved. But even then the possibility remains that, through magnification of an elementary process, macroscopic behavior also becomes indeterminate. These discoveries in physics are of great significance for fundamental research in biology. In all probability, pure physics and biology are merging into a higher unity in this area, jointly pursuing the essence of life.[8]

Man is one subject of biological study. Biology teaches us that every animal body consists of cells. A body grows through the multiplication of its cells. This multiplication takes place through the duplication of the cell nuclei. The cell nuclei contain chromosomes consisting of peculiar giant molecules which, because of their structure, bear the name deoxyribonucleic acid (DNA). These giant molecules have spiral structures and the remarkable ability to create their own twins, which become the nuclei of new cells. DNA possesses the simplest form of life, that is, the ability to reproduce itself. Each DNA molecule is comparable to a large card file, the individual cards of which record in atomic script all the qualities and hereditary traits of the being as a whole. The cells combine into units for purposes of division of labor and pursuit of certain goals. Of special importance are the germ cells which permit sexual reproduction and the brain cells which control the entire way of life.

Sexual reproduction starts with the combining of a sperm cell and an egg cell. In man, this results in a new combination of some 25,000 genes from both parents. Enormous varieties of combinations are produced. But each of them is subject to the Mendelian laws of heredity. Since this has been true since primeval times, one can understand the well-known materialistic conclusion that man is but a deterministically controlled combination, programmed since primeval times, and that no place remains for control by God or "spirit." But this conclusion will no longer stand up, for the giant molecules in the reproductive cells carry the hereditary traits in the form of combinations of atoms—"atomic script," as we said above. As we have shown in some detail, the law of causation and strict determinacy does not apply in the atomic world. A scientifically unpredictable reaction can occur in some nucleus or shell, producing what we call a mutation. Due to multiplication and heredity, the mutation has colossal impact. It takes its place in every body cell of that being and of all its descendants. It cannot, as such, be annulled. These elemental events occur only in accordance with Planck's law of energy quanta. When events occur in an atom, the energies involved can jump only by the amount of these energy quanta. That is why we speak of quantum leaps and why this field of biological research is known as quantum biology.

Not all quantum leaps have the same value. The question of where they occur in the reproductive cells is of importance. Only in rare places do quantum leaps lead to the developmental progress of the life form; in all other cases, their effect is harmful or even fatal. In primeval times, when there were no men in the present sense of the term, there may have been life forms whose hereditary substance contained such an accumulation of quantum leaps (i.e., mutations), produced by abnormally strong cosmic radiation, that millennia of pairings of the resulting life forms developed choice forms, through Darwinian selection, which led biologically to modern man. It is, of course, equally possible that a single quantum leap of a particular kind with a subsequent chain reaction of quantum leaps in a single life form was the direct cause of the development of man.

If we think back to primeval times and then look ahead from there in the light of quantum biology, we see that the way things in fact developed could not have been predicted. We can assign no cogent scientific reason for the unique mutation, perhaps occurring in only a single life form, which led to the development of man, for we cannot see through the curtain drawn before our cognitive faculties. One can, however, understand the statement that, viewed from behind the curtain, these developments could and did follow God's plan. At this point physics truly has room for the assertion that a creation by God took place. Physics leaves room for such an assertion, but the assertion itself is *not* a matter of physics; it is a matter of theology alone.

I consider it unlikely that the further development of mankind can be described in terms of physics and biology alone. In any case, such a description would not suffice for theology, which makes an additional assertion: "Man became a living soul" (Genesis 2:7; I Corinthians 15:45, A.V.). The soul inhabits the biological body and has been endowed with a spirit by God. At the end of a long period of development, controlled purely biologically, God created man in His image. However, in John 10:30, Jesus says, "I and the Father are one." Man, then, is created in the image of Jesus, and is bearer of a spirit as creative as God and Jesus themselves. The spirit, which has its origin in God, is not created after the manner of the biological body; rather, it is conferred and lent. It manifests a continued direct participation in God. In words later endorsed by Jesus in John 10:34, Psalm 82:6 affirms, "You are gods, sons of the Most High, all of you."

I do not believe that this spirit was irrelevant to the biological development of man. If man had lacked it, his body would not have been strong enough to survive the conditions of environment and selection in the Darwinian sense. Unlike beasts, man does not exist by bodily weapons and instincts alone; only because of his spirit is he able to endure. Only because of his spirit has he risen above the animal kingdom and, as instructed, become lord and master of nature. Our body is of this world alone; our spirit is of this world *and* the world beyond. Our spirit offers us the only chance we have to learn and experience something of what lies beyond the curtain that is drawn through all nature, and hence through every atom in our body. Actually, we live in two worlds. We control what happens in this world with something from the other. In this matter we are not totally free, for we cannot leave our bodies; but we are not totally chained, either, for we can master our bodies. We are bound by the limitations of our bodies, but we are free to the extent of the scope allowed us by the indeterminacy of atomic processes and the inapplicability of the law of causation as previously understood.

That our bodies die is a statement and a fact of both physics *and* theology. That the soul and spirit do not die can be a statement of theology only. Only the New Testament refers to the death of the soul, "the other, second death"; but that is beyond the scope of this book. No one knows how the spirit is structurally related to our bodies; but the fact of the relationship is not contested. Could the thing we call the soul be the principle that binds body, life, and spirit? The Scriptures leave no doubt that redeemed man is only spirit-man, not soul-man. This is the chief lesson of Jude's epistle. As verse 19 says of those who destroy the community from within, "It is these who set up divisions, intellectual (or mental), devoid of the Spirit. But you, beloved, . . . pray in the Holy Spirit" (Jude 19-20). I have translated literally from the original Greek text. In many translations, the word "intellectual" or "mental" (*psychikos*) is unfortunately rendered as "worldly," thus depriving this passage of its meaning. The passage is significant also for the evidence it offers that the concept of an immortal soul, as treated in Greek and idealistic philosophy, is alien to the Scriptures. Paul alludes to the same problem in I Corinthians 2:14-15. These are not simple problems, but we should—indeed, we must—be concerned with them.

We have said that the spirit controls our bodies. In doing so, it can use its own discretion. But if the spirit belongs to the other world, it operates right through the curtain which we, with our intellectual powers of this world and our physical devices, are unable to penetrate. The curtain is impermeable in the sense that one cannot physically slip through it. But theologically it is a finely knit fabric permeable to the spirit. The human spirit does not die. In heaven and hell we shall know of each other and meet each other again. But we cannot, without further consideration, identify the organs that give us our abilities of sight, hearing, and cognition with the structures and functions of our earthly, mental bodies.

There is more to be said of the freely willed decisions made through the spirit. In doing so, we hark back to biological facts, and specifically to those dealing with the functional agglomeration of cells called the brain. All circuits from the various sense organs and points of desire and pain—i.e., all the nerves—end in the brain. Energy, functioning solely in quantum form, is carried on each circuit. Similarly, all energy in the central brain, which stores, switches, signals, and transforms, also functions solely in quantum form. In other words, even if we knew nothing about the structure of the giant molecules in the brain, every single impulse carried on a circuit is dissected into a large number of quantum leaps. There may even be nothing left at the end of an impulse but a single labelled quantum leap. After the energy of an impulse is thus received, analyzed, and dissected, a reverse process, containing the reply or defensive reaction to the primary impulse, may (and very often must) occur.

In countless cases, a stimulus elicits an automatic, clear response. But many times a man's actions do not appear to be practical, necessary responses to external stimuli; rather, they flow from the internal motivation of the spirit. The spirit must make use of the atomic structure of the brain and the body. The processes (energies) stored in the countless atoms of the brain molecules, in a manner analogous to the law of radioactive decay which we discussed in section 6a of chapter 7, have long half-lives governing their entry into action. Since in the case of a single process this entry into action is totally undetermined by nature, the spirit has considerable leeway to make a thing, which is physically indeterminate and subject to no law of physical causation, come to pass at a time and place of its choice. Originating at an extremely minute atomic point, a chain reaction then occurs which ultimately leads to a large-scale event, i.e., movement or speech.

Let me reiterate that the strict old law of causation does not apply to the single atom. This does not mean, of course, that no causality at all applies to the atom. Where physics ends, theology begins. Where causality ends physically, it begins in the higher, theological sense with the efficacy of the spirit. Theology received through revelation what it tells us about the spirit. Revelation is that which is transmitted from the other side of the curtain. What it tells us is that the human spirit is a bit of God's Spirit, as the Bible says in Proverbs 20:27, "The spirit of man is the lamp of the Lord, searching all his innermost parts." If even this small element is able to control the human mind and body, then how much more is God's perfect Spirit, which we call the Holy Spirit, able to control them! Thus, God in his Holy Spirit can have effect everywhere. He is an infinitely close God, not a distant one.

One should take serious note of the clear lesson of quantum physics that man does not have the nature of a machine or a computer, determined and programmed in the materialistic sense. Though this is not its task, quantum physics precisely identifies the limits of our physics, beyond which free will, the human spirit, and the Holy Spirit can intervene and control. At this frontier, every person must decide for himself whether or not to follow a call from the other side. Apprehension has occasionally been expressed that the repeal of the law of causation in the atomic kingdom denotes a tendency toward disorder and arbitrariness, thus challenging the concept of God. But the true concept of God is not challenged. Events in the universe are linked to the applicability of Planck's constant, an absolute constant of nature. This absolute constant governs order *and* freedom. It gives valuable insight into a much-discussed theological problem, for it shows how God, despite his absoluteness, leaves free will to humans.

I have interpreted the modern field of quantum biology theologically. An exact scientist may, of course, not take this liberty while engaged in his scientific work, but a theologian should and must do so. There are also other reasons why he should not ignore quantum biology. It apparently can make a significant contribution to our understanding of the miracles performed by Jesus, and occasionally by his followers, on the sick and especially on addicts and possessed and insane persons. We are of course able to effect some cures today by a full application of physical and chemical methods, but in many cases these methods are unsuccessful.

It is obvious that the Spirit of Jesus had a potent effect on the sick. A power emanating from Jesus' body awakened slumbering powers in the sick man's body—if the sick man's mind was prepared to let them operate and did not resist them. Here again a single quantum leap may be the key that unleashes a recovery avalanche. But the leap occurs only if the spirit in the mind of the sick man wills it or, to express it quite differently, if the sick man's spirit opts for unreserved faith. What happens at that atomic point which is the key to the whole? The process is not objectifiable, and the classical law of causation does not apply to it. The energies and other requirements for the quantum leap are all available, but whether it takes place is, as section 8 has indicated, totally indeterminate from the standpoint of physics. But the religious spirit allows the leap to take place, leading to the avalanche of inner events that restore order to the sick man's mind and body.

It is Jesus who performed these miracles. But if they are consonant with natural law, as was indicated in chapter 6, they must still be possible today. It is understandable that young people have been known to free themselves suddenly of the worst bondages, which the New Testament would call demonic, while hospitals and welfare agencies with their medications and physicians stood helplessly by. Jesus, after all, is not just a personage of the past; he is also a holy spirit of the present. His Holy Spirit tells our spirits that we are God's children. To accept that in complete faith is to become healthy.

VIII. BIBLICAL THEOLOGY EVALUATED IN THE LIGHT OF PHYSICS

1. COMPLEMENTARITY IN THE MICROCOSM AND THE MACROCOSM

I was recently surprised to learn, as I read Shakespeare's play, that what Hamlet says to Horatio is, "There are more things *in* heaven and earth, Horatio, than are dreamt of in our philosophy." From hearing and seeing this quote countless times in German translation, I had always thought that the words were, "There are more things *between* heaven and earth than our school wisdom lets us dream of." The statement as Shakespeare wrote it does not raise any problems. That which is *in* heaven is the subject of theology and not of physics. That which is *on* earth is the subject of scientific research, which has yielded results beyond the wildest dreams of our ancestors. In its popular German version, however, the sentence clearly presents the problem that troubles us. What about the area between heaven and earth, what about the limit or curtain that we discussed above? Theology and physics are not irrelevant to each other. Both place demands upon men. They meet and overlap in his heart and in his mind. *Between* heaven and earth is where man is. The spirit operates out of the other world, while the biological body operates out of this one. We inhabit two worlds at the same time. One is spiritual and religious, the other is material and biological.

We have repeatedly spoken in the preceding chapters of the area between earth and heaven. Many future discoveries are hidden on the earthly side, close to the border area; this is where theology has its best connections with physics. Physical research has moved from the macrocosm, visible to the eye, to the invisible, mysterious microcosm. In so doing, it has found that the non-causal laws of the microcosm bear a statistical relationship to those of the macrocosm. Niels Bohr's concept of complementarity is of great importance for description of the knowledge that has been gained. As we pointed out earlier, this is the concept summarizing the fact that one and the same thing—namely, the energy in atoms and quanta—appears either as a physical identity in a narrowly limited space or as a spatially extended wave field and oscillating state. The two faces of this entity seem contradictory to our minds and, if both were to exist simultaneously, would appear irreconcilable. This complementarity was discovered in the microcosm.

The word complementarity sounds complicated and unpleasant to the layman. It is not a household word. At most, he may have heard that there are complementary colors, that is, pure colors which, to the eye, appear white when combined. Examples of such pairs are orange and ice blue, yellow and navy blue, or red and blue green. It is thus a matter of rounding out or completing. The layman has generally found it easy to accustom himself to scientific discoveries that lead to technically useful inventions. He should not have difficulty in accepting the discovery of a concept that clearly describes some known facts. But theologians should take an even greater interest in this concept, for complementarity is a principle on the order of the "energy principle," the "entropy principle," the "principle of the least effect," and the "principle of evolution." A scientific "principle" is a final, generally applicable, fundamental truth, deriving from a vast abundance of experience. It is comparable to the axioms of mathematics which, as David Hilbert has shown, cannot be reduced to simpler form, and from which nothing further can be deduced.

As we indicated several times in this book, the miracles and the miraculous language of the Bible, particularly in the New Testament, contain essential features of complementarity. We shall return to this subject in the following sections. But all the stories in the Bible relate to events in the macrocosm. This poses in sharp fashion the question of the relationship between the complementarity that was discovered in the microcosm and the complementarity that is observable in the macrocosm. To detect a mere analogy between the two would not be satisfying. This problem of physics can be approached in different ways. One may start with the hypothesis that the microcosm and the macrocosm are separated, not by a sharp dividing line, but by a very wide transitional region. One would then study the complementary behavior of matter, moving gradually from individual elementary processes to processes involving ever larger numbers of particles. In our discussion of problems of causality we referred to chain reactions and avalanches initiated by individual atoms and leading to effects in the macroscopic world. In such cases one member of the complementary pair now becomes active.

One may also proceed in the opposite direction. One starts with the apparently complementary features of macroscopic phenomena and seeks their origin by penetrating to their microcosmic building blocks. There is also a third approach, used by this author in his experimental research. He has found that de Broglie's matter-wave equation, which so effectively underlines the essence of complementarity, can properly be applied in the case of large numbers of particles, that is, in the macrocosm, as well. It has a cybernetic effect in these cases, and is visible in rhythmic physical, chemical, and particularly biological reactions. In other words, Planck's constant is a value that governs not only the microcosm in the narrow sense but the macrocosm as well.

Knowledge that is based on considerable experimentation is summarized effectively in the concept of complementarity. Yet a certain obscurity is inherent in the concept. That is not a disadvantage, however. It expresses the fact that much remains to be discovered in this area, perhaps through the working out of the physical problems described above. No less a man than Niels Bohr took care in his lectures and works not to define the concept of complementarity too sharply or to interpret it too narrowly. He was fully aware that the concept was of fundamental significance for various problems of biological life and psychology, and in a far broader sphere as well, especially theology. We might some day discover that the concept of complementarity unites not just two manifestations of energy in the microcosm and the macrocosm but also a third manifestation still unknown to us. Though the two we know belong to the inorganic realm, the third could lie in the domain of organic life. The theological concept of the Trinity may hint at something of this sort. From the purely scientific viewpoint, however, this is at the present time merely a hypothesis without experimental foundation.

2. THE TRINITY[10]

The very thing that in physics has been regarded as an unprecedented innovation for half a century and that seems to place unreasonable demands on man's intuitive powers has been experienced and accepted as reality by the Christian community since its founding. Professional physicists have long noted that their findings in quantum physics take a form that was once reserved to theology—indeed, that was once regarded as the very characteristic of theology.

Note how the two compare. Physics: The foundation of nature is energy, which manifests itself in spatially confined corpuscles or in oscillating states. Theology: The primary cause of all being is God, who manifests himself either personally, in the person of Jesus or in the Holy Spirit, or as a movement among his people.

In making this comparison I by no means wish to indicate that the modes of speech of physics and theology are ultimately the same; that would be a variety of existentialist theology. Nor do I mean that the evidence used in one field can be construed as applying to the other. But in these modern times "modern" theological circles should at least take note that the Trinity "God, Jesus, Holy Spirit" appears to be reflected in the triad "energy, corpuscle, wave." In any case, by acquainting themselves with the language of physics, modernistic theologians could learn that biblical language is not so "old-fashioned," "mythological," "absurd," "incomprehensible," or "based on an outdated world view" as they like to pretend.

Let us look a little more closely at the affinity between the theological Trinity and physics and between the concepts of complementarity that each of them hold.

Jesus was a historical person. His second advent in human form as an exalted master is awaited and will come to pass. Acts 1:11: "Men of Galilee, why do you stand looking into heaven? This Jesus, who was taken up from you into heaven, will come in the same way as you saw him go into heaven." Regarding the relationship between God and himself, Jesus says that he is the Son and was not created. "I and the Father are one." "He who has seen me has seen the Father." "My Father is working still, and I am working." In the same or a similar way as energy acts in all the corpuscles of matter, and as all matter is ultimately energy, so God acts through Jesus, and Jesus is God.

In the interval between the Resurrection and the Second Coming, Jesus as a person is not visible. Yet theology teaches he is present in the complementary sense, through the Holy Spirit. "I will dwell among you"; "I am in you and you are in me"; "I am with you always, to the close of the age." As God acts through Jesus, so he acts through the Holy Spirit. The analogy is that energy acts in all light waves. So significant is the action of Jesus through the Holy Spirit that to blaspheme the Holy Spirit is to deny Jesus.

The New Testament speaks of the Holy Spirit in a decidedly complementary manner. It states that Mary conceived the Child of the Holy Spirit, i.e., as of a person.[12] This is a way of saying that Jesus condescended to become an embryo, that he was born through the labor of his mother, that he lay on his mother's breast as a helpless infant, that he grew up as all children grow, and that he partook totally and completely of the development and appearance of a human being. When Jesus says in John 14-16 that he will not leave his disciples but will send the Holy Spirit to them as a Comforter, he speaks of the latter as of a person. The Greek work for Comforter is *parakletos*—literally, the man who stands by (*para*) and is called upon to give comfort (*kletos*). Jesus identifies himself with the Holy Spirit.

On the other side of complementarity, the Holy Spirit appears not as a person, but as a state that penetrates men, spreads in waves over the earth, and sets hearts to joyful vibration. This is marvelously expressed in the pentecostal experience of the first congregation. It came over them like storm waves, and the Holy Spirit had the effect of flaming light and speaking in tongues. How often has it been said in revival movements since that time, "They were filled with the Holy Spirit."

The members of the early Christian congregations were people like us. They had the same difficulties of understanding and intuition as we have when they contemplated the things I have just described. But they let themselves be guided by the Holy Spirit, which they could experience, feel, and see at work each day. They did not bar themselves to him. The basic thesis of Professor Bultmann's demythologizing theology—that "the world view of the New Testament is mythical"—was unknown to them. Rather, they obeyed the instructions given by Peter in his second letter (II Peter 1:16): "For we did not follow cleverly devised myths . . . but we were eyewitnesses of his majesty." Similarly, Bultmann's contention that "what the New Testament says of the 'Spirit' and of the sacraments is alien and incomprehensible" would have lacked validity for the members of the early congregations.

Instead, the spiritual struggle of the early churches, the apostolic fathers, and the church fathers led to the three great confessions of faith, which offer guidance for all time—the Apostles' Creed, the Nicene Creed, and the Athanasian Creed. In them, Christian theology formulated the essence of the Trinity and struggled to express properly that which in physics is called complementarity. This struggle is most clearly manifested in the Athanasian Creed, which can be regarded as a sort of commentary on the Nicene and Apostles' Creeds. I shall cite a few of its sentences: "We worship the one God in his Trinity and the Trinity in his unity without mixing the persons or dividing God's essence. . . . the Father eternal, the Son eternal, the Holy Spirit eternal. And yet they are not three Eternals, but one Eternal. . . . Similarly there is God the Father, God the Son, God the Holy Spirit; and yet these are not three Gods, but only one God. . . . In this Trinity there is no earlier or later, no greater or lesser, but all three are equally eternal and identical."

3. THE DEVIL AND DEATH

The Bible employs the language of complementarity in other regards as well. God's great antagonist is the Devil. His essence is not made apparent in the word as it exists in our language. In the Greek New Testament he is called *diabolos,* which literally means "confuser." The confuser appears in the Bible either as a person or as a state.

As a person, the confuser also bears the Hebrew name Satan, or antagonist of God. He also is called Beelzebub, or god of the flies, for he controls the swarms of flies connected with plagues. As a person he appears before God in the Book of Job, and God at first gives him a free hand. As a person the confuser appears before Jesus in the desert and uses quotations from the Bible in an effort to seduce him from the true path. Since that time, many people have allowed themselves to be totally misdireced by biblical quotations taken out of context. Jesus is called upon for many reasons nowadays, but not for the reason for which he was crucified. As a person the Devil was first found and later tossed into the abyss (Revelation 20:2, 10). Just as Jesus as a person has various names, so there are several excellent descriptions of the Devil as a person—e.g., "ruler of this world" (John 14:30), "father of lies" (John 8:44), "accuser of our brethren . . . before . . . God" (Revelation 12:10).

This is the side of the confuser that we like to portray in caricature as a satyr with horns and tail, thus deceiving ourselves. Understandably, many people today are repelled by this incarnation of the Devil as a person and deem the doctrine of the Devil a superstition. But they are unable to shunt aside the complementary form of the Devil; indeed, they appreciate it. The Devil dwells less conspicuously among us in another form—as a state of our hearts and flesh. Just as the Spirit of the Lord has access, as I stated above, to each atom in our body, particularly to those in our heads and hearts, so the confuser, too, has access to them. With his access to every atom in our bodies, he is able, as the demonic power of this world, to obstruct our links with God's world (cf. Revelation 12:9). That is how sinfulness dwells in our flesh, constantly confusing us and forcing us to do the evil we do not want to do and to abstain from the good we would like to do. Just as God's Spirit dwells in men who have opened themselves to him, so the spirit of the confuser—also called the spirit of this age (Ephesians 2:2)—dwells in other men. Just as the Holy Spirit is the complementary manifestation of the person of Jesus, so is the spirit of this age the complementary manifestation of the person of the Devil. Our world is filled with this spirit, which sometimes reaches the point of mass demonic behavior, the frenzy of war, and the dissolution of all moral order and propriety. Its effect is recognizable also in the use of talismans, fortune-telling, and horoscopes, and in the perversion of such concepts as democracy, peace, education, and social behavior into mere slogans and phrases. The methods of power employed by the spirit of this world change from century to century, and sometimes from decade to decade, but the power behind them does not change. In the words, "Do not be conformed to this world," the New Testament admonishes us not to establish our abodes in the being of the confuser. Nowadays we do not see the person of the confuser in sharp outline; rather, we experience his contemporary form in the state of confusion besetting our hearts and minds.

The Bible speaks of death in the same complementary manner as it uses in speaking of the Devil. And we do the same.

In his first epistle to the Corinthians, Paul calls death a foe. According to the sixth chapter of the Revelation, it rides like a person on a bloodless horse. In Revelation 20, death and hell are cast into the fiery pit. The extent to which death is pictured as a powerful person is indicated by our frequent representations of it as the reaper.

On the other hand, death appears as a state, for we must die. It accompanies us from inception. We evolve into it. An old hymn begins, "In the midst of life we are embraced by death." It is planted in all our bodies. It overtakes us in the atoms and molecules of our body organs. Aging is a form of dying prior to death itself. What death actually is, however, remains a physical and biological mystery. With good reason some researchers are looking for active molecular materials with which dying is ultimately connected. Death may be hidden in just a few molecules. But we do not know.

4. THE RESURRECTION

It was not the purpose of this brief book to discuss details of the accounts of the biblical miracles. I have touched upon that subject elsewhere.[13,14] My purpose here is to raise fundamental questions, causing us to reflect on whether biblical theology and physical knowledge are not interrelated as revelations of the Creator, while biblical theology and modernistic theology are far removed from one another. Not only has the evolution of physics brought us to a frontier where, for the seeker of truth, theology begins and theology alone can take us further; it has also made many miracles real or plausible. Our research still has a long road ahead of it; large areas remain unexplored. But we already know enough to make us stand in reverence before the Bible and take to our own hearts the statement in Luke 2:19: "Mary kept all these things, pondering them in her heart." We should ponder the knowledge of physics and theology in our hearts, so that each field may make the other more fruitful.

A modernistic theologian, on the other hand, has defined his task as that of "cleansing the Christian message of such pagan myths as the Virgin Birth,[12] the Resurrection, and other dogmas." This is not usually stated so openly. Rather, the preacher usually delivers a sermon that is fine in form and exposition; but he casually mentions along the way that the story that is the subject of his sermon is only a legend. The idea that Jesus' disciples and the ancient Christian community projected their belief in the risen Christ, with whom they had some now but faintly remembered experience, back to their association with the man Jesus during his lifetime, is viewed as a marvelous discovery of our century. It is alleged that, for this projection, they invented countless miracles, legends, and mythical portraits.

I would find it quite understandable if someone were willing for psychological reasons to accept many lesser miracles as relevant, while questioning the great miracle of the Resurrection. But one who denies all the lesser miracles and deems them to be myths cannot possibly take seriously the mighty miracle of the Resurrection. Whatever he may do to reinterpret the biblical stories, one thing is certain—for him, the Resurrection and the Lord's subsequent association with his disciples do not constitute a reality that is also physical. I personally view Jesus' resurrection as a reality and await my own rising from the dead and my own resurrection as a reality for the simple reason that, to me, death, too, is a bitter reality, not a legend. As a sober, thinking physicist, I have no use for a mere new interpretation derived from considerations of human life and death, for I cannot eliminate death by wishful thinking.

In referring to Jesus' resurrection as a "reality that is also physical," I am borrowing a phrase from the language of science. This phrase helps us today to state most cogently what, in addition to the purely spiritual message, the New Testament says about the Resurrection. Many preachers discuss the Resurrection as if there were no physical reality connected with it. They sometimes say that, while Jesus was actually living prior to his crucifixion, he was no longer living after his resurrection on Easter morning. I cannot agree. Whenever the New Testament speaks of Jesus' resurrection or the testimony to his resurrection, it speaks of an event in this world of nature and not just of a spiritual event. Between his resurrection and his ascension, Jesus had the same natural sort of association with his disciples as he had had before. If we translate the word "natural" into a word deriving from the Greek, it is "physical." When Paul, in the first epistle to the Corinthians, enumerates several appearances of the risen Christ, he is referring to something entirely real, not to something symbolic, allegorical, or psychological. What he says can and should be questioned. One will then find that the testimony of the disciples is that Jesus lingered among them, spoke and dined with them in the old way, once again discussed with them the theological meaning of all that had been written about him and of his acts and statements during the three years he had spent with them. And all this took place within the normal framework of relationships among people. This typical reality constituted the first proof to the disciples that something serious and real was intended by the statements about their own rising and resurrecion.

The physical reality of Jesus' life and work before the Crucifixion on Good Friday differed from that after the Resurrection on Easter morning in only one way: before the Crucifixion, Jesus lived as our fellow-man in the same reality as that in which we live today, whereas after the Resurrection he also could live—and especially after the Ascension he did live—in a higher reality which, because of our sinfulness, is not yet accessible to us, but which is not in conflict with his natural laws. We, too, when we rise, are going to live in that higher reality. But the reestablishment of our old earthly bodies is absolutely unnecessary for that purpose. What will rise again is a "spiritual body," but a "body" nonetheless.

The fact that Jesus' resurrection is attested to not only as a spiritual and religious reality, but also as a physical reality, should keep us from indulging in the nebulous conjectures which many theologians describe today with the words "something happened, but it is no longer comprehensible." As Paul says, if Christ was not really resurrected, seen, heard, and touched, then everything remained as before, and we remain with our sins, in addition to being the worst of self-deceivers.

One year, in a city on the Werra, I heard an Easter sermon of dismaying feebleness. After reciting the great passage on the Resurrection in I Corinthians, the preacher stated that all of our old ideas and interpretations on the subject should be put aside. Even Paul, he said (and at this point the pastor actually lied), did not personally experience anything relating to Jesus' resurrection, and had to rely on the reports of others. In the United States, he continued, an experiment had been conducted in which mentally ill youths were locked in a room and allowed to rant and rave at each other and at the walls until they had exhausted all the protest that was within them. They then seemed to be redeemed and liberated; they had the impression of being alive for the first time and of having been resurrected from their earlier state. One who knows anything at all about psychology, the pastor continued, knows that this is the sort of experience that the first Christian communities also had, and that this is the only way their experience can be understood. The Resurrection, then, was something psychological, and in this way Christian doctrine tries to help us achieve a new life.

Modernistic theology never tires of downgrading the story of the Resurrection by arguing that the Resurrection was not a historical event and that no one really witnessed it. Now, physicists did not witness the great events of the earth's past history, either; yet these were real historical events, with after-effects and consequences of which we try to make good use. What happened in the grave and how it happened is quite unimportant. What really counts is the fact that Jesus associated with his disciples, taught them, and ate with them for forty days thereafter. He who personally experienced that does not need to fabricate legends or to project them back to another time.

Our certainty that the stories of the Resurrection are true derives from the power current of the Holy Spirit which flows in the New Testament, leading us into the miracles of the first group. But modern physics also offers us some assistance in regard to the event of the Resurrection. It has made a small contribution for our consideration and edification. It has informed us of the curtain that is drawn around us, blocking our vision into the world beyond. True, our ability to explain is inadequate; but neither can we demonstrate any violation of natural law. Physics leaves open the possibility that Jesus, as the Son of God, can, through his Spirit, have impact from the other side of the curtain. When Jesus' body lay in the grave, his Spirit was alive. Preaching in and with that Spirit, he visited the kingdom of the dead, also known as the nether world, to lead its inhabitants, too, to salvation. The early church considered this message so important (I Peter 3:19 and 4:6, and other old accounts) that it was included in the Apostles' Creed.

Let no one protest that the period of one or two days, measured by earthly standards, was much too short for coverage of the entire nether world population. We are wont to argue that, though almost 2,000 years have passed since then, only a fraction of the world's population has been reached by Jesus' message. Time as we measure and experience it is linked to the matter and space of this earth, as we explained in section 2 of chapter 7. But the inhabitants of the kingdom of the dead are spirits, no longer bound to earthly bodies. It is therefore senseless to apply our concept of time to this biblical assertion about the nether world. To put it in the language of physics, the relativistic conversion ratio between earth time (one or two days) and nether world time is unknown to us and never can be known to us on earth.

Physics does not tell us—and never will be able to tell us—how many "compartments" there are in the world beyond, i.e., in heaven, the world of the dead, and hell. But there is one thing we can say: that a man can be there only in his spirit, not in his earthly body. When our Lord died on the cross, his body was still on earth, but his spirit was still not in God's heaven or, as he put it, with his Father. And when he arose from his grave and associated with his friends, he was still not with his Father. This is what he meant when he said to Mary Magdalene that he had *not yet* ascended to his Father (John 20:17). Not until the Ascension did he join his Father.

Our Lord, when resurrected but not yet ascended to heaven, had a body with properties, including an ability to transubstantiate, that astound us. He existed, so to speak, in the region between heaven and earth, to use the phrase we introduced earlier. The matter in his body could apparently dissolve into nothing or, to state it better, into invisibility. And it could do the opposite as well. Must we conclude that this conflicted with natural law? Atomic physics has taught us that matter can resolve into invisible radiation and that—the other way around—radiation can become matter. In fact, there is serious discussion today about the possibility that matter in large galaxies draws together and disappears as matter and, contrarily, rises from the interior and evolves further. It is dubious that "nothingness" plays a role in this. It would be preferable to speak of visibility and invisibility, or measurability and nonmeasurability. To the physicist, of course, the world visible to the eye is but a small part of a large invisible reality. But energy, which can assume many guises, is active everywhere. The circumstances determine in which of its complementary forms energy will manifest itself.

What happened in the grave at night is no less miraculous than what happened in broadest daylight—Jesus entering closed rooms, disappearing before the disciples on the way to Emmaus, appearing to James, and showing his wounds to Thomas. Interestingly enough, nowhere does it say that Jesus walked demonstratively *through* closed doors. Rather, he suddenly appears in the midst of his friends. The curtain, after all, is everywhere, not merely in doors and walls. One does not pierce it by normal earthly methods.

I should like to point out also that a resurrected body may be so diverse in its energy compositions that it may at times be unable to come into contact with our earthly bodies. Similarly, on earth it is sometimes possible to have contact with one energy form but not with another of the same magnitude that is derived from it. This is why the Lord warned Mary at the grave not to touch him, while on another occasion Thomas was actually told to touch him.

CONCLUSION

As we explained in the Foreword, this booklet is an apologetic, intended to defend the Christian faith against doctrines that reinterpret and depreciate its central propositions and miracles. Among the means used by influential modern theologies to reinterpret and depreciate Christianity is the application of scientific propositions in forms totally incompatible with physics today.

In this defense, the author, a professor of physics, has considered it proper to explain at the outset what he personally means by theology and what he believes in. His theology is founded on the propositions of St. John's Gospel, Genesis, and the Apostles', the Nicene, and the Athanasian Creeds. Perhaps all feeling for this ancient theology—in no way new—has been lost in many churches. Perhaps it is regarded as old-fashioned and disagreeable, and is no longer understood by young theology students. But this cannot prevent the author from going back to the original, rock-hard foundations in theology, just as he is used to doing in his basic research in physics. Then, in his way, he seeks to show, mainly on the basis of the rediscovered meaning of verse 31 of the creation story in Genesis 1, how the relationship between theology and physics can be dealt with through the examination of the problem of miracles.

In our discussion of miracles, to the extent that they can be studied today from the viewpoint of physics, we refrained from presenting detailed interpretations (of the sort provided in[13,14]); rather, we described the pertinent overarching principles of statistical processes and quantum physics, derived from our knowledge of the atomic structure of matter. We further indicated that the concept of explanation of nature must give way to the more modest concept of description of nature. Considering the cognitive limits to which physics has led us, it is incumbent upon us to confine ourselves to the observable and the measurable, since we cannot give any explanation in the true, deeper meaning of the term.

Theological truth and physical reality are both addressed to one and the same person. He must therefore ponder both of them in his heart and in his mind. The reader must already feel challenged to look more deeply into the basic questions of physics, since "modern" theologians are not in the habit of doing so for him, although they really ought to be. In this brief outline, however, we could not delve into all the problems raised by the miracles, nor could we illuminate any more biblical stories simultaneously from the standpoint of the theological Trinity and the complementarity of physics. The reader must continue his thinking for himself; and he can and should challenge my views. All I would ask of him is that he read the Bible carefully and examine the foundations of physics with equal care. By careful reading of the Bible I mean not only picking out the sentences one finds congenial in one chapter, but interrelating all that is said on the subject throughout the Bible, even if some of it seems mutually contradictory. What appear to be contradictions usually arise from the misconceptions under which one labors and which one imparts to the text. Careful study of physics does not mean blind acceptance of old materialistic views but acquaintance with the status of physics in our century, as grounded in recent experiments. The bibliography at the end of this book may be helpful in this regard.

BIBLIOGRAPHY

Bibliographical notes are to the German editions used by Prof. Schaaffs; in some cases, English translations are also available.

1. Niels Bohr, *Atomphysik und menschliche Erkenntnis* ("Atomic Physics and Human Knowledge"), Vol. I, 2nd impression (Braunschweig: Vieweg, 1964).

2. ———, ibid., Vol. II (Braunschweig: Vieweg, 1966). Bohr introduced the principle of complementarity in physics. He won the Nobel Prize for Physics in 1922.

3. Hans Bender, *Parapsychologie, ihre Ergebnisse und Probleme* ("Parapsychology: Its Results and Problems"), 2nd impression (Bremen: Schünemann, 1970). Bender, a professor at the University of Freiburg, presents a sober description, free of superstition and psychosis, of phenomena that our present knowledge of nature is insufficient to explain.

4. Louis de Broglie, *Licht und Materie, Beiträge zur Physik der Gegenwart* ("Light and Matter: Contributions to Contemporary Physics"), (Frankfurt: Fischer-Bücherei, 1958). De Broglie is the discoverer of particle waves, which gave importance to the concept of complementarity in physics. He won the Nobel Prize for Physics in 1929.

5. H. Haag, A. Haas, J. Hürzeler, *Evolution und Bibel* ("Evolution and the Bible"), (Freiburg: Herder, 1962).

6. Werner Heisenberg, *Wandlungen in den Grundlagen der Naturwissenschaft*, ("Transformations in the Foundations of Natural Science"), 9th impression (Stuttgart: Hirzel, 1959). Heisenberg discovered the uncertainty principle. He won the Nobel Prize for Physics in 1934.

7. Pascual Jordan, *Der Naturwissenschaftler vor der religiösen Frage* ("The Natural Scientist and the Religious Question"), 5th impression (Bremen: Stalling, 1968). Jordan has produced significant work on quantum physics. This extensive treatment reaches to the limits of physics in an effort to break down old walls between

religion and natural science, but takes no position on specific theological issues.

8. ———, *Schöpfung und Geheimnis* ("Creation and Mystery"), (Bremen: Stalling, 1970). This book is a valuable complement to the preceding, but can stand alone. The relationships to Christianity are more clearly evident.

9. Bernhard Philberth, *Christliche Prophetie und Nuclearenergie* ("Christian Prophecy and Nuclear Energy"), 7th impression (Stein am Rhein: Christiana, 1969). The declarations of the last book in the Bible, Revelation, allegedly full of fantastic mythology, have taken on a terrifying reality in our own time.

10. ———, *Der Dreieine* ("The Three-One"), (Stein am Rhein: Christiana, 1970). Subtitled "Beginning and Being: The Structure of the Creation." Philberth develops a world view in which theology, natural science, and philosophy are interwoven. His book is challenging reading.

11. Hans Rohrbach, *Naturwissenschaft, Weltbild, Glaube* ("Natural Science, World View, Faith"), (Wuppertal: R. Brockhaus, 1967). This little book is valuable for information about fundamental world views. Its author is a professor of mathematics.

12. ———, *Geboren von der Jungfrau Maria* ("Born of the Virgin Mary"), 2nd. impression (Stuttgart: Goldene Worte, 1969). This booklet contains a confession of faith in the reality of the biblical accounts and in the creeds.

13. Werner Schaaffs, *Christus und die Physikalische Forschung* ("Christ and Research in Physics"), 3rd impression (Berghausen: Evangelisations-Verlag, 1969). This book refutes the assertions of the theology of demythologization, gives the Christian testimonies of several great natural scientists, and explains a number of miracles.

14. ———, *Jesus, Meister der Natur* ("Jesus, Master of Nature"), 2nd impression (Wuppertal: R. Brockhaus, 1971). The New Testament statements about Jesus as the Creator form the focal point of this presentation. There is a detailed discussion of the Creation accounts, of the principle of evolution in physics and biology, and of the problems of descent. Distorted views of modernist and fundamentalist theology about nature are discussed.

INDEX

99